W9-CHZ-254

The Cautionary Scientists

Other Books by Kenneth S. Davis

Fiction

IN THE FORESTS OF THE NIGHT
THE YEARS OF THE PILGRIMAGE
MORNING IN KANSAS

Nonfiction

SOLDIER OF DEMOCRACY
RIVER ON THE RAMPAGE
A PROPHET IN HIS OWN COUNTRY:
   The Triumphs and Defeats of Adlai E. Stevenson
THE HERO:
   Charles A. Lindbergh and the American Dream
WATER, THE MIRROR OF SCIENCE
   (with John A. Day)
EXPERIENCE OF WAR:
   The U.S. in World War II

KENNETH S. DAVIS

The Cautionary
Scientists

PRIESTLEY, LAVOISIER, AND THE
FOUNDING OF MODERN CHEMISTRY

G. P. Putnam's Sons   New York

947632

ST. PAUL PUBLIC LIBRARY

© *1966 BY KENNETH S. DAVIS*

*All rights reserved. This book, or parts thereof,
must not be reproduced in any form without permission.
Published simultaneously in the Dominion of Canada
by Longmans Canada Limited, Toronto.*

Library of Congress Catalog Card Number: 66-15580

PRINTED IN THE UNITED STATES OF AMERICA

Contents

Introduction

In our time it has become all too easy to regard science as a vast impersonal force—a kind of Frankenstein's monster that, escaping human control, has forcibly seized us and carries us at terrifying speeds in directions we have not chosen toward ends unknown.

One reason for this is that the knowledge science develops is wholly impersonal, rigorously objective. Unlike the products of creative art and, to a lesser degree, of speculative philosophy, the scientist's work is not a unique individual self-expression whose appreciation by others is also a form of self-expression. On the contrary, the fruits of science are a public information that is precisely the same (that is, has the same meaning of itself alone) for all who share it, no matter how greatly they vary among themselves in character, location, and past experience.

Moreover, the history of science contains many instances in which important discoveries have been made independently and almost simultaneously by two or more scientists. This suggests that at every stage of scientific development, save perhaps the first, there are certain discoveries that are virtually inevitable, being ready and waiting and even crying to be made. They exist as active possibilities; they practically force themselves on the attention of investigators; and to the extent that they are determinative, science becomes something that has happened and continues to happen automatically—a process that, once launched, has a momentum and direction of its own. To this extent the individual scientist is but a mechanical element or passive function (in the mathematical sense) of the progress he apparently creates. Insofar as he is necessary to this progress, it is in much the same way as a physical event in a causal sequence, itself an "effect," is necessary as "cause" to the event that follows it. This conclusion seems sustained by the fact that from a purely scientific point of view, human beings *are* only objects in a world of objects: They are phenomena of mechanics and electromagnetic force, particular instances of general laws whereby their responses to stimuli, by becoming predictable, become controllable.

The sense of science as monstrous inhuman force is yet further encouraged by the manner in which scientific research is generally conducted today. Huge accelerators, nuclear reactors, electronic computers, telescopes, radar installations, and rockets designed to probe with men and instruments the hitherto secret depths of space—these are the giant tools now employed, and one of their effects has been to take scientific research out of the hands of solitary individuals and place it, instead, in the hands of immense impersonal organizations. The rate at which new scientific knowledge will be gained and applied can be forecast fairly accurately in terms of the amount of money assigned to the organizations conducting the research: The larger the annual budget, the faster (generally speaking) new discoveries will be made. Inescapable and omnipresent are the technological effects of this research: jet planes flying well beyond the speed of sound, television, fifty-megaton thermonuclear bombs, satellites shining bright as Venus in the evening sky, and automated factories and transportation systems. More and more, as a result of scientific technology, the economic activities through which individual men formerly expressed themselves while earning their bread—activities that made the individual important to the economy and gave social significance to his life—have been and are being shifted to machines of such complexity as to be incomprehensible by most minds.

Nor is there much use in protesting what seems to many people a dehumanization of the world, a downgrading of the value of the individual life. This sad effect is a concomitant of scientific progress, and "progress is inevitable."

What this amounts to, of course, is an abdication of individual moral responsibility for the uses to which scientific technology is put. It means a divorcement of living wisdom from naked physical power. "The leaders of the modern world are drunk with power," wrote Bertrand Russell in *The Scientific Outlook;* "the fact that they can do something no one esle previously thought it possible to do is to them a sufficient reason for doing it." [1] Faced with the possibility of some new world-transforming technical achievement, men have almost ceased to ask *why* the possibility should be realized. Will its effects be good or bad, measured by a reasoned scale of human values? Will it increase man's happy security on earth or, instead, his terrified insecurity? Such questions seem to most men futile, since their answers have no practical effect. If a thing can be done, it will be. The only effective question to ask of it is, *How?*

Indeed, the substitution of *how* for *why* in questions asked of the natural world was a principal characteristic of the birth of modern science, about three and a half centuries ago. An initial stimulus of this development was the rediscovery in western Europe of authentic texts of certain ancient scientific treatises, notably those of Archimedes (287?-212 B.C.) and Aristarchus (315?-230? B.C.). The seminal ideas contained in these Greek treatises had failed to flower in ancient Rome, with its slave economy and its concentration on business, government, war, and sensual pleasure to the virtual exclusion of intellectual curiosity. But in the Europe of the sixteenth and seventeenth centuries the same ideas fell as viable seed on rich soil—a soil prepared for the sowing by a variety of cultural and economic forces.

Among these was the Christian Church. This seems paradoxical and was certainly inadvertent. History records that the leaders of the Church early recognized in the rise of science a threat to their authority and did all they could to prevent it. But if the Church forcibly insisted that Faith be the master of Reason, it also insisted that the source and object of this faith was a supremely rational Being who operated, not in sporadic bursts of wrath and benevolence as did the Jehovah of the early Hebrews, but in accordance with Divine Law. The latter, believed to be both decreed and obeyed by God, was actually derived by men, in its essential spirit, from the legal structure of Republican and Imperial Rome. Hence, it was "the child of philosophy," to quote Lecky's *History of European Morals*. The Roman law "was ... formed upon the philosophic model," continued Lecky, "for, instead of being a mere empirical system adjusted to the existing requirements of society, it laid down abstract principles of right to which it endeavored to conform...." [2]

The principles were those of the Stoic philosophy, whereby man's moral code was identified with the natural order. They were expressed in a very famous passage by the Roman Cicero—that master lawyer of a race of lawyers. "True law is right reason in agreement with nature, worldwide in scope, unchanging, everlasting ...," he wrote. "We may not oppose or alter that law, we cannot abolish it, we cannot be freed from its obligations by any legislature. ... It does not differ for Rome and for Athens, for the present and the future; ... it is and will be valid for all nations and all times...."

This concept of universal order—this sense of all things and events as part of a fully articulated system—is literally catholic. By preserving and extending it in the West, the

Church maintained through the medieval period what Alfred North Whitehead has called an "instinctive... faith in the possibility of science." Priest and scientist were bound to disagree, violently at first, on the way in which the world order must be known: The Church's dogmatic pronouncements must often be flatly contradicted by science's discoveries, but the disagreements and the contradictions rested on the shared assumption that there *is* an order with objective laws that are in some real sense knowable by the human mind. In the absence of this assumption modern science could not have developed, as, in fact, it failed to develop in the otherwise creative, immensely sophisticated civilizations of India and China.

Another force preparing the way for science was social and economic. Here, too, the Church played initially a major role, insofar as its teachings were those of Jesus as quoted in the New Testament. Slavery as an economic institution and Christianity as a moral code are essentially antithetical; as the latter grew in persuasive force, the former waned. The replacement of slave by free labor in mines and mills and fields and in the workshops of the towns; the development of the free market, with its complex of interdependent specialties, as a means of stimulating and distributing production; and the consequent development of complex systems of money and credit—all these introduced to the economy a vastly increased incentive toward laborsaving and cost-reducing devices while removing a stigma formerly attached to all forms of work with one's hands. Manual skills began to be regarded with respect; mechanical invention and scientific experiment were alike encouraged.

Note, for instance, the concern for the welfare of miners which permeates Agricola's famous treatise *De re metallica,* published in 1566. In the long history of mining this aspect of Agricola's work marked a new departure. For thousands of years men had been laboring under the earth to extract metallic ores, but in former times these men had been slaves, driven by the lash, and so cheaply replaceable that their owners, unburdened by a Christian conscience, had felt no urgent need to protect them from the hazards of their labors. Agricola felt this need urgently indeed. "A miner," he wrote, ". . . ought to be a good and serious man. . . ." He closed the sixth book of his treatise with a section on "the ailments and accidents of miners, and the methods by which they can guard against these." Most of the sixth book dealt with problems of pumping and ventilation, problems which grew acute as deep-shaft mining was developed and coal was introduced as fuel in the last half of the sixteenth century. They were problems requiring investigation into the nature of "air," which—since it was sometimes explosive, sometimes smothering, and sometimes poisonous—could no longer be regarded as a simple and invariable "spirit." These investigations laid the foundations for the science of pneumatic chemistry; upon them were built the scientific careers of the two men with whom this book is concerned.

The point now to be made is that the Church-dominated medieval synthesis, its center a clearly defined relationship between God and man, had by Agricola's time largely broken down. The synthesis had been the culmination of a struggle to conceive a universal law and order, and since this struggle had been rooted in what is evidently a basic continuing need of men, a new struggle for order was now under way. But the new struggle was rooted in a different aspect of the basic need. It took, therefore, a radically different form.

In the medieval period and, for the most part, in the classic period before it, the struggle had been toward a single systematic answer to all questions of *why*. Why are things shaped as they are? Why do they move as they do? In sum, why man and the universe? In the modern period, which was given its essential definition in the seventeenth century, the struggle is toward a single systematic answer to all questions of *how*. How are things shaped? How do they move? In sum, how (or on what principle) do man and the universe operate? In the medieval period philosophers who concerned themselves with natural phenomena were primarily concerned about classifying these in categories of mind. In the opening modern period scientists are increasingly concerned, not with classification, but with measurement in rigorously objective ways. Their very observations become forms of measurement, made with increasingly precise and ingenious instruments.

Of this substitution of *how* for *why* in questions asked of the natural world and of the consequences of such a substitution, a highly significant example is provided by the work of Johannes Kepler of Germany (1571-1630). He was a figure of transition between medieval and modern, partaking of both. He was an astrologist, as well as an astronomer; a kind of sun worshiper, as well as a pious Lutheran. His mind became a field of battle between mysticism and logic and, in regard to logic, between the deductive method that dominated philosophy in his day and the scientific inductive method that was partially defined by Francis Bacon of England (1561-1626) and established in practice by Galileo Galilei of Italy (1564-1642) while Kepler lived. Of his strange story, the presently relevant part has to do with the manner in which he conceived the basic idea of his greatest contribution to science.

The idea, nourished by a Christian faith in Divine Law, was rooted in the number mystique of the Greek Pythagoras (*circa* 530 B.C.). The ancient Pythagoras had been impressed, even obsessed, by the harmony and proportion which "ruled," in his view, the universe. He was especially enthralled by the way in which music could be reduced to arithmetic, tones being represented by numbers and harmonic intervals by numerical ratios. "All things are numbers," he concluded, meaning that the whole universe is organized in terms of sequences and regularities that can and indeed must be expressed in numerical (mathematical) terms. He conceived the universe to be a living sphere at the center of which is the earth and around which the planets, each with its distinctive tone, revolve at speeds and distances that make for a "music of the spheres."

It was a Pythagorean "intuition" that flashed upon the twenty-four-year-old Kepler one day in July, 1595, telling him that the universe is built along the lines of perfectly symmetrical geometric figures, the earth and the celestial bodies being placed, in motion, at proportionate intervals of these lines. Because there are six and only six planets, five intervals exist between them, the intervals being so numbered because there are five and only five "perfect" solids—that is, three-dimensional figures of which all the faces are identical in shape and size. It was fortunate for Kepler's "intuition" that the existence of the smallest planets was then unknown. It was fortunate for science, too, since the "intuition" suggested to Kepler a number of testable hypotheses. From one of these, making use of the remarkable astronomical observations of Tycho Brahe (1546-1601), he ultimately derived his famous Three Laws describing the motions of the planets, a fundamental of the great structure of physics and astronomy which was completed three-quarters of a century later.

But—and this is the significant point—he did not derive these laws until he made a radical change in the *kind* of question he asked concerning planetary motion. One of the fascinations of his work is the manner in which the answers he was led to by his initial questions of *why* were at last overcome by the ruthless logic of his observations of *how*. Why do the planets move as they do? Because God, a perfectly rational Being, wills it. Therefore, the planets must describe perfectly circular orbits around the sun. Kepler had to wage a long hard war against this "innate" idea before he could derive his First Law, which states that each planet describes, not a circle, but an ellipse, one focus of which is occupied by the sun.

Galileo, a much more "modern" man than Kepler, avoided Kepler's greatest difficulty by refusing, explicitly, to deal with questions of *why* at all. "I don't think this is a seasonable time to enquire into the cause of the acceleration of natural motion . . . ," he had Salviatus say in *Two New Sciences*, whose publication is generally believed to mark not only the founding of modern dynamics (the science of motion) but also the firm establishment of the method which has since been predominant in science—a method combining quantitative experiment with mathematical demonstration. Galileo pointed out that this question of cause was one "concerning which philosophers have greatly differed in opinion" and went on: "But as to our author, it is enough at present that . . . [he] search out and demonstrate to us some passions * of an accelerated motion (let the cause of that acceleration be what it will. . . .)"

By proceeding in this way, Galileo was enabled to eliminate as unnecessary concepts of "cause" which had been obstacles to the progress of physics for thousands of years. For instance, the age-old answer to the question of *why* inanimate objects move had been, "Because something pushes them"—the prime mover being God—an answer containing the implicit assumption that it is somehow more "natural" for things to be at rest than in motion. The assumption was avoided by Galileo. He stuck to the

---

* The "passion" Galileo refers to has nothing to do with human emotions but is instead what *Webster's Dictionary* defines as the "state or capacity of being affected by external agents or forces. . . ."

obvious fact that some things move and others remain at rest, and he arrived at the demonstrable conclusion that they will persist in the state they are in—that is, will re- main at rest or in uniform motion along a straight line— unless a something called "force," which he does not attempt to explain, operates on them. This "natural" per- sistence, or tendency to remain the same, in regard to the "state" of motion, is called inertia, a property common to all objects. Galileo's definition of it is the law of inertia. It is also known as the first of Newton's Three Laws of Motion.

Isaac Newton (1642-1727), born in the year Galileo died, completed the mighty structure for which Kepler and Galileo provided the fundamental materials. He did so by inventing mathematically a means of joining the celestial mechanics of Kepler with the terrestrial mechanics of Galileo in a single all-embracing and perfectly coherent system. His means, as everyone knows, was the Universal Law of Gravitation, which states that "any two bodies in the universe attract each other with a force which is di- rectly proportional to the product of the masses of the two bodies and inversely proportionate to the square of the distance between them." The structure it completed must be thought of in mechanistic, rather than architec- tural, terms. "How does the universe work?" asked West- ern man. Newton, standing on the shoulders of earlier giants—notably Kepler, Galileo, and Descartes—replied, "It works as a machine, its moving parts being solid objects that possess inertia and are linked together by an attractive force whose intensity, in any particular instance, varies in terms of the masses and distances involved."

In the quantity and quality of its historical effects no other single triumph of human thought can compare with this grand design, this immense illumination. It applied alike to the infinitesimal and the infinite. It shed light on vast areas of former darkness, where terrors had lurked, breeding cruel superstitions. In 1600 most people, regardless of education, still believed in the existence of witches, in portents, and in the possible practice of magic and sorcery. In 1700, hardly any literate person so believed, and none among the best educated. In the latter, thanks to science, the medieval outlook had given way completely to the modern.

Men at the close of this amazing seventeenth century might feel that although not quite everything in the natural world had already been explained, the terms in which the explanation must ultimately be made had been firmly established. So was the way in which the explanation must be sought. The terms were essentially those of mechanistic theory; the way was the compound of induction, deduction, and experiment we now call "scientific method."

In these terms and in this way, Harvey (1578-1657) by then had discovered the circulation of the blood; Gilbert (1540-1603) had explained the directive motions of the magnetic needle on the assumption that the earth acts as a gigantic lodestone; Leeuwenhoek (1632-1723) had developed microscopy, discovering protozoa and bacteria; Leibniz (1646-1716) and Newton, independently, had invented (or discovered) integral and differential calculus; Halley (1656-1742), had, with Newton, calculated the orbits of certain comets (those "fiery portents" of former times) around the sun; Roemer (1644-1701), on the basis of observations of Jupiter's moons, had proved light to have a finite, if immense, velocity; Huygens (1629-95) had developed the wave theory of light, while Newton developed a rival corpuscular theory; and Robert Boyle (1627-91), pioneering the science with which this book is chiefly concerned, had not only discovered the law of gaseous properties which bears his name, but had also given the first clear definitions to the chemical terms "element," "compound," and "mixture." The list of men and triumphs could be much further extended.

Simultaneously, as part of the whole process, there had been great advances in the development of scientific instruments. The compound microscope, the reflecting telescope, the liquid thermometer, the barometer, an efficient air pump, the pendulum clock, improved marine instruments of all kinds, and unprecedentedly precise scales and balances—all these, unavailable at the end of the sixteenth century, were at hand for the use of scientists by 1700. Also, first steps had been taken toward an organization of scientific effort—toward the formation of an international community of scientists who stimulated one another's researches and promoted a quick publication of research results. Periodicals devoted wholly to science had been initiated, and most important of all, the two great scientific societies of western Europe, the Royal Society of London and the French Academy of Science in Paris, had been founded and were flourishing.

Small wonder that the eighteenth century opened in western Europe "with a quiet confidence [among leaders] that at last nonsense had been got rid of"—to quote Whitehead again—or had been *almost* got rid of. Assuredly bigotry remained in the world. Errors were institutionalized in society, government, religion, and education. But the bigotry and the errors were deemed to be lingering shadows of the Dark Ages, which steadily contracted as the area of enlightenment steadily widened. Anxiety-breeding ambiguities and faiths whose assertiveness was proportionate to the doubt at their core were either banished or in the process of banishment wherever one looked, their places taken (or about to be taken) by demonstrable certainties.

Since the scientific habit of mind is a measuring habit,

it inculcated in leading minds that idea of "progress" which has remained central to the Western outlook ever since. The idea implies the existence of a rigid scale of measurement, standing somehow outside the stream of historical development, whereby this development can be seen to move from lower to higher or from worse to better. So conceived, progress seemed to most leading minds bound to continue at an accelerating rate into a limitless future. Apropos is a statement made at the height of the eighteenth century by a Protestant minister, who was also one of the most famous scientists of his time and one of the two protagonists of this book. "Whatever was the beginning of the world," Joseph Priestley said, "the end will be glorious and paradisiacal, beyond what our imagination can now perceive." The attitude he bespoke was already prevalent in educated minds at the century's birth. The Age of Reason, ruled by the laws of nature and nature's God, had begun.

Many people in our time are inclined to look back on this age with nostalgia, seeing it as in many ways a happier time for human beings than the present Age of Anxiety. By concentrating on the *what* and *how,* men launched a tide of scientific technological power, which has flowed with constant augmentation and continuous acceleration into the twentieth century. By increasingly neglecting questions of *why* as far as they required answers in terms of human or divine purposes, men also initiated the process whereby the physical power born of science, as it grew, was to become increasingly divorced in several respects from vital (that is, emotionally informed) intelligence: To the extent of this divorcement it was to become a force as independent of individual desire and as indifferent to human values as the tides of the sea or the tremors of the earth or the storms of the atmosphere. But the process was yet in its opening phases, the tide of power still comprehensible and manageable by individual men, as the Age of Reason reached its zenith. Science, relatively new in the world, was yet a function of men working for the most part alone—an obviously *human* activity, motivated by *human* curiosities and purposes toward ends clearly beneficial to all mankind.

Moreover, these individual men were by no means completely absorbed by their scientific function. They approached science as gifted amateurs, rather than as career professionals. If science was their major interest, it was only one interest among many. They maintained a balance in their lives between the intellectual and the emotional—between the self which looks out on the world of objects, describing them and their relationships with logical rigor, and the self which feels its way into the world as an organism, at the same time feeling intensely its own identity. They were, in other words, *whole* men—complete, self-sustaining individuals—as few men in our age of interdependent specialties and specialists find it possible to be.

Two such men are the subject of the book that follows—one an Englishman, named Joseph Priestley; the other a Frenchman, named Antoine Lavoisier. Major attention will be paid to their work as scientists, which is much more easily understood than the advanced work of our day in the areas wherein they pioneered. They dealt directly with sensible objects—things a man can see, touch, hear, taste, and smell—rather than (as scientists nowadays generally do) with the signs of signs of signs of existences no man can ever perceive in themselves. They made little use of mathematics as a tool of their research or as a language for the communication of their research results. For this very reason a close look at their work may reveal to those who are mathematically untrained—as a similar look at today's highly specialized and abstract sciences could not possibly do—what it is that characterizes natural science in general and distinguishes it from other ways—the poet's way, for instance, or the religious mystic's way—of dealing with the external world.

The book will also seek to convey some sense of the historical importance and philosophical significance of the science of the two men. Certainly their work has this importance and this significance. It is important historically because it made major contributions to the progress of science. It is significant philosophically because it exemplifies the manner in which systematic knowledge is developed out of empirical knowledge and determines, after its development, the character of all subsequent intellectual effort along the same lines.

Finally, the book will deal, in terms of its two protagonists, with the development of science in relation to and as part of the general history of mankind; it may suggest a proper balance between *how* and *why* in dealing with the problems rising out of the scientific technology of today. Each of the protagonists was very much a living part of his times, vitally affected by (and effecting) dominant streams of social change in the eighteenth century. Each shared the prevailing optimism of the Age of Reason, believing in the perfectibility of man through proper education, in the ultimate triumph of reason in all areas of human activity, and (generally) in the absolute good of inevitable progress. Yet both, ironically, were deeply injured—and one of them was actually destroyed—by violent expressions of the irrational elements of human nature to which neither in his philosophy had given sufficient weight. Thus, an account of their lives and times may point up the need to heal the breach that has opened in modern man between emotion and intellect—between the part of man that feels concretely, apprehending the world directly (intuitively), and the part of man that abstracts and analyzes, dealing with the world in terms of general laws whereby its phenomena become predictable and, to an increasing extent, controllable.

Certainly this breach is wider today, and more dangerous, than ever before. It causes men to mistake means for ends in ways that may (since they can) destroy all life on earth. Measured by the scale of human values to which most men pay lip service, science as the pursuit of knowledge for its own sake is a positive good because it enlarges the human spirit. By itself scientific knowledge is indifferent to human values. But the power born of this knowledge, like all other kinds of power, tests the character of those who wield it. "Power is not one of the ends of life but merely a means to other ends," wrote Bertrand Russell, "and until men remember the ends that power should serve, science will not do what it otherwise might to minister to the good life." Nor can science itself define the ends it should serve, Russell went on to say. These lie in the "sphere of values"—which itself "lies outside science, except insofar as science consists of the pursuit of knowledge" —and on this sphere "science as the pursuit of power must not obtrude." [3]

To this may be added Lord Acton's remark that all power tends to corrupt. The overcoming of this tendency in men who now have in their hands, thanks to science, hitherto undreamed-of and rapidly increasing power is the great moral challenge, the great political and social problem of our age.

The Cautionary Scientists

1. Joseph Priestley:
From Fieldhead to Bowood

A Yorkshire Boyhood

Joseph Priestley was born in the parish of Birstall, not far from Leeds, in the northern English county of York, on March 13 (Old Style), 1733. (The Gregorian calendar now in use was not adopted in England until 1751, when Joseph Priestley was eighteen. Thereafter he celebrated his birthday on March 23.) The house of his birth, called Field-head, was a small two-story structure of stone, with a slate roof. In architectural style it was not unlike Shakespeare's birthplace in Stratford-on-Avon, and it may have been almost as ancient; certainly it had been in the possession of the Priestley family for generations.

He was the eldest of six children—four sons, two daughters—born to Jonas and Mary Swift Priestley at the rate of one a year until she died "in the hard winter of 1739, not long after being delivered of my youngest brother," as Joseph wrote in a memoir for his own children a half century later.[1] She was, he then recalled, "a woman of exem-

25

plary piety," a Presbyterian (Calvinist) like her husband, and was beautifully sustained by her faith during her final ordeal. Her last words related to a dream she had just had of "a delightful place, which she particularly described, and imagined to be heaven." She said, "Let me go to that fine place!" Joseph was then only six years old. He had been taken, while yet an infant, to live at his maternal grandfather's farm near Wakefield, some miles from his birthplace. Hence, his mother was ever a shadowy figure to him.

Jonas, his father, however, was well remembered. Joseph returned to his father's house following his mother's death, when his place was taken at Grandfather Swift's by the youngest Priestley child. Three years later, aged nine, he was adopted by his Aunt Sarah (Mrs. John Keighley, his father's sister) and went to live at Old Hall, the Keighley house at Heckmondwike. He continued to see much of his father, however, for Old Hall was only a brisk forty-minute walk from Fieldhead.

By trade Jonas was a weaver and cloth finisher; by nature he was remarkable for his evenness of temper, cheerfulness of disposition, and healthiness of physique. "He had uniformly better spirits than any man I ever knew," his famous son said of him in later years, recalling him not only as he was at the height of his modest prosperity but also as he was when, an old man, he was reduced to an impoverished dependency on his children. No doubt his living example helped develop in the son the serenity of spirit—the calm conviction that all was for the best in the long run—which later characterized the son in times of adversity. He must have taught this by precept, too, for he was a deeply religious man, who held morning and evening prayer sessions with his family. His religious faith, after all, had the doctrine of predestination at its heart, and his sanguine temperament could hardly have failed to translate this from a gloomy fatalism into a sunny acquiescence.

Indeed, a serenity and stability almost incredible in our day and remarkable even in that day characterized nearly all phases of life in the West Riding of Yorkshire while the boy Joseph Priestley was growing up—a serenity and stability encouraged by the landscape, the local tradition, and the simple economy. Green valleys were tucked between high steep hills, atop which were grouse-filled moors rolling in long waves of wind, austerely beautiful, under a wide sky. Yorkshire countrymen were notoriously self-reliant and liberty-loving (most of them had been on Parliament's side in the Civil War), and their truly rugged independence of the rest of the world enabled such people as the Priestleys to dwell in the midst of historic turmoil "[as if] in some far-distant planet," to quote Mme. Belloc, a great-granddaughter of Joseph's.[2] Since medieval times Yorkshire had been a center of the woolen industry, and the loose family-centered organization of this industry had persisted virtually unchanged for generations in the hills west of Leeds.

The handloom weaver did his work in his home—hence, the name "homespun" applied to his product—and quite often he was a small farmer as well, keeping a cow and a horse, raising fowl, cultivating a narrow field or two, and raising each year a substantial kitchen garden. Fieldhead was such an establishment, and Jonas Priestley, according to local custom, loaded a packhorse once a week with his homespun and took it into Leeds for market day. There, in a town which had a population of about 16,000, he dealt with merchants who funneled Yorkshire woolens into the world market, but for the most part even his market-day contacts were confined to his own sober, industrious, God-fearing kind.

When Joseph joined the Keighley household, he entered

a much wider world, richer in possibilities and far more stimulating to his intellect, than would have been open to him in his father's house. John Keighley was a man of considerable property. He was also a man of vigorous mind, who had earned his religious convictions through thought and spiritual struggle. It is said that in his youth he had been a persecutor of the Calvinist Dissenters from the established Church of England and whose services were then illegal and had gone so far as to inform civil authorities of the times and places of Dissenter meetings. Indeed, it was with the intent to persecute (so the story goes) that he secreted himself in a worship place of Dissenters, one night or day, only to be converted by what he saw and heard from his hiding place. Then, "instead of delivering the minister up to punishment, he took him into his own house, and supported him, till the iron arm of intolerance was broken, and people were allowed to worship the God of their Fathers according to the dictates of their own conscience," according to an article published in *The Universal Theological Magazine* in April, 1804.[3] His direct influence on young Joseph, however, was slight, for he died within a year or two after the boy came to live at Old Hall.

But the prosperous widow, Aunt Sarah, influenced Joseph Priestley profoundly in his boyhood—and for the good, he was happy to record in his memoir. Having no children of her own, she became "truly a parent to me, till her death in 1764," he wrote. She was, he further wrote, "a truly pious and excellent woman, who knew no other use of wealth, or of talents of any kind, than to do good, and who never spared herself for that purpose." There was no taint of intolerance in her piety. She was "far from confining salvation to those who thought as she did on religious subjects," so that her house became a "resort of all the dissenting ministers in the neighborhood without distinction, and those who were most obnoxious on account of their heresy were almost as welcome to her, if she thought them good and honest men (which she was not unwilling to do), as any others." Thus, the boy heard many discussions of theological questions in his home and no doubt imbibed also the liberal political attitudes which were so marked in him later on.

The aunt hoped and believed that her nephew was destined for the ministry. The boy concurred. He became notably devout, kneeling in prayer not only at bedtime, as his younger brother Timothy later reported, "but in the course of the day," and going without fail one night each week to the nearby Independent Chapel, there to pray and converse with other young men. Timothy was also much impressed by Joseph's ability to repeat the whole of the Assembly Catechism "without missing a word" and by the fact that he devoted nearly all his free time to serious reading and study; "from eleven to about thirteen he had read Mr. Bunyan's works and other authors on religion, besides the common Latin authors." [4] (According to his own account, *Robinson Crusoe* was the only romance he read before he was nineteen.) All his education was pointed toward the ministry in the several schools he seems to have been sent to as a boy in Heckmondwike. In these he learned Greek and Latin at an early age, and under the tutelage of the local minister, during school holidays, he learned Hebrew.

But he failed to take enough out-of-doors recreation, and when he was in his mid-teens, he fell seriously ill. It was a chronic illness that had many of the symptoms of tuberculosis. He was forced to drop out of school and, for the time being, to abandon his plan of entering the ministry. It was decided that he should instead prepare himself for trade.

Although the circumstance seemed tragic to the boy and his aunt at the time, it enabled the adolescent boy to pay much-needed attention to his physique and allowed his superior intellectual resources to be more fully employed for two years than they would have been, had he been confined to a school curriculum. Moreover, a large portion of his attention was perforce turned from spiritual to practical matters, preparing him for the work which was to bring him lasting fame. He taught himself French, Italian, and German, becoming sufficiently proficient in the first and last to write and translate letters in them for a merchant uncle. Simultaneously he learned Chaldean and Syriac and began to read Arabic. From a highly educated local Dissenting minister, Mr. Haggerstone, whom he visited twice a week, he learned geometry, algebra, "and various branches of Mathematics, theoretical and practical" and was encouraged to read "Gravesande's *Elements of Natural Philosophy,* Watts's *Logic,* and Locke's *Essay on the Human Understanding,*" as his memoir recorded. Meanwhile, his health steadily improved. At the end of two years it was decided that he was well enough to "resume" his "former destination for the ministry."

To such "resumption," however, there was an obstacle: As his body and mind grew stronger, his faith in strict Calvinist doctrine grew weaker. Indeed, on crucial points of doctrine his faith was destroyed altogether, killed by too much analytical introspection. The Assembly Catechism he had learned by heart as a child said: "All mankind, by the fall of our first parents, lost communion with God, are under His wrath and curse, and so made liable to all miseries, to death itself, and to the pains of hell forever." But Joseph Priestley discovered that he did not and could not feel, personally, the slightest guilt or repentance for Adam's fall. At first he suffered immense pangs of guilt for his failure to feel guilt, but he ended by denying that there was valid cause for the latter, especially since the alleged consequences of original sin outraged his sense of justice and contradicted his conception of God's loving-kindness. Similarly, but with less spiritual anguish, he had lost his faith in the doctrine of the Holy Trinity. It seemed to him needlessly complicated—so complicated indeed as to be beyond his comprehension: It violated a logical principle of identity, which otherwise prevailed over all of God's universe. He therefore rejected the idea of the Trinity in favor of the idea of God's simple and perfect unity.

He became, in short, what is known by theologians as an Arian (after Arius of Alexandria, *circa* A.D. 330) and an Arminian (after Jacobus Arminius of Holland, 1560-1609) —a heretic and a subversive by the standards of the elders of the church in which he had always worshiped. When he made formal application for admission as a communicant to this congregation, his application was refused by these elders, although the minister, Mr. Kirkby, who had long regarded him as a protégé, was willing to receive him.

In the normal course of events he should have prepared for his ministry at the Academy in a place called Mile End, but (in his own words) "I resolutely opposed it, especially upon finding that if I went thither, besides giving an *experience,* I must subscribe my assent to ten printed articles of the strictest Calvinist faith, and repeat it every six months." At this point Mr. Kirkby fortunately intervened. He, being well educated, had small use for the kind of narrowly dogmatic teaching practiced by the orthodox Calvinists at Mile End; he urged Mrs. Keighley to send her nephew to the much more liberal Daventry Academy, which had been founded (in a different location) by Dr. Philip Doddridge in 1729 and which was now headed by Dr. Ashworth. "My good aunt, not being a bigoted Calvinist, entered into his views." Joseph Priestley, accordingly, was enrolled at Daventry in September, 1752.

The Education of a Dissenter

The Dissenter Academies were children of necessity, born because the doors of the great universities were legally closed, upon the restoration of the monarchy, to all who were not members of the Church of England. The government's purpose was, of course, to discourage the spread of Nonconformist doctrines, but the salutary effect was to provide both the incitement and the opportunity to shape a new kind of formal higher education, one much better suited to the new world created by seventeenth-century genius than the kind of classical learning preserved through clerical tradition, out of the Middle Ages, at Oxford and, less exclusively, at Cambridge. Priestley described the case defiantly but accurately, years later, in a communication to a Prime Minister of England:

> Shutting the doors of the universities against us, and keeping the means of learning to yourselves, you may think to keep us in ignorance and so less capable of giving you disturbance. But though ignominiously and unjustly excluded from the seats of learning, and driven to the ex- pedient of providing at a great expense for scientific edu- cation among ourselves, we have had this advantage, that our institutions, being formed in a more enlightened age, are more liberal and therefore better calculated to answer the purpose of a truly liberal education. Thus while your universities resemble pools of stagnant water secured by dams and mounds, ours are like rivers which, taking their natural course, fertilise a whole country.[5]

Certainly the Daventry Academy was almost perfectly suited to his need and temperament during the three years (from the age of nineteen through the age of twenty-one) that he studied there. Dr. Ashworth was an orthodox Trin- itarian but no more a bigot than Priestley's Aunt Sarah, or he could not have retained as his principal assistant

Samuel Clark, who was a Unitarian and openly subscribed to several other heretical views. Both Ashworth and Clark were relatively young men, humble in their realization that they had students who were their superiors in some branches of learning. (Priestley was among those; he was so far advanced by the time he entered that he was promptly excused from all the studies normally required for the first year and from most of those required in the second.) Hence, there was much give-and-take between teacher and pupils, an anticipation of the "discussion method" of teaching, which has come into vogue in our century. The general plan of study was deliberately designed to encourage independence of judgment and a hostility to dogmatic authority in all matters of thought and conscience. Each student was required to read authors on both sides of key questions and to prepare digests of the arguments for future reference. The whole spirit of the place was one of free enquiry. "... the students were about equally divided upon every question of much importance, such as Liberty and Necessity, the Sleep of the soul, and all articles of theological orthodoxy and heresy," said Priestley, "in consequence of which all these topics were the subject of continued discussion. Our tutors were also of different opinions. ..." Small wonder that he "saw reason to embrace what is generally called the heterodox side of almost every question."

The Academy curriculum differed from Oxford's or Cambridge's because the students were taught not only mathematics, history, and other traditional subjects but also natural and experimental philosophy. (The term "science" did not acquire its present academic meaning until early in the following century.) Thus, Priestley's interest in natural phenomena and his bent toward experimentation were probably encouraged, but certainly not with the effect of causing him to reconsider in the slightest his "destination" for the ministry. His dominant interest, then and later, was theology.

Indeed, the attitude toward science which he developed at Daventry and retained all his life, although fairly typical of the eighteenth century, seems strange today. Priestley had no exalted opinion of the scientist's vocation. "Let it be remembered," he wrote years later, "that a taste for science, pleasing, and even honorable as it is, is not one of the highest passions of our nature, that the pleasures it furnishes are even but one degree, above those of sense, and therefore that temperance is requisite in all scientifical pursuits." In this he followed David Hartley (1705-57), whose *Observations on Man* (1749), which Priestley read at Daventry, exerted a profound and lasting influence on him. Hartley wrote in this book: "Nothing can easily exceed the vain-glory, self-conceit, arrogance, emulation, and envy, that are found in the eminent professors of science. . . . Temperance in these studies is, therefore, evidently required, both in order to check the rise of such ill passions, and to give room for the cultivation of other essential parts of our natures." Nor did Hartley (any more than Priestley) leap to this conclusion out of an innate hostility to science or from any fear of scientific conclusions. On the contrary, his exceedingly bold major effort was toward making psychology (then called "pneumatology") a branch of physical science. His book endeavored to explain all mental phenomena as the effects of purely physical causes.

What most deeply impressed Priestley in Hartley's philosophy was its basic doctrine of necessity. Hartley argued that all that happens, evil as well as good, is God's will operating exclusively through a mechanism of cause and effect. Yet God is infinitely good. Hence, the chain of cause and effect leads inevitably to a glorious end, and the discerning eye of piety can discover in "all partial evil, universal good." A mind long-fed on Calvinist predestination, as Priestley's had been, was well prepared to receive this new and far happier doctrine, and Priestley's naturally sanguine temper was sustained by it, serene in the midst of adversities, through the rest of his life.

Preacher and Teacher

He encountered adversity at the very outset of his career. One cause was an inherited impediment to his speech, which caused him sometimes to stammer painfully. This had not seriously handicapped him until now, when it became a formidable obstacle.

Upon the completion of his studies at Daventry his first call was to a small and impoverished congregation at Needham Market, in Suffolk. He accepted it after stipulating that no part of his salary should come from the orthodox Independent fund, which had theretofore been joined with the Presbyterian fund and the local congregation to pay the meager salary of forty pounds a year. The stipulation involved him in grave economic difficulties. His congregation, initially promising to supply the salary deficiency caused by the refusal of Independent help, failed to keep its promise, and since Priestley's Aunt Sarah was forced by other demands on her purse to halt her remittances to him at this time, he would have starved, as he said, had he not received "now and then an extraordinary five pounds from different charities."

He remained at Needham Market for three bleak years, from 1755 to 1758. During this time he was exposed to hurts that would have destroyed the self-confidence of a man less buoyed up than he by optimistic faith. His small congregation grew smaller still when it was discovered or when he revealed that he was no Trinitarian. The orthodox were, of course, outraged. His painful speech delivery made him unwelcome in neighboring pulpits and militated against his receiving another and better call. He was lonely. "I felt the effect of a low, despised situation, together with that arising from the want of popular talents," he later wrote (although he also insisted, characteristically, that he was "far from unhappy at Needham"). He went on to write:

> There were several vacancies in congregations in that neighborhood where my sentiments would have been no objection to me, but I was never thought of. Even my next neighbor, whose sentiments were as free as my own, and known to be so, declined to make exchanges with me, which . . . he acknowledged was not owing to any dislike his people had to me as heretical, but for other reasons, the more genteel part of his hearers always absenting themselves when they heard I was to preach for him.

Small wonder that he grew a little desperate. He tried to start a school for children but obtained no pupils, "not that I was thought to be unqualified for this employment, but because I was not orthodox." He then proposed a series of lectures for adults on various branches of science at a fee of half a guinea for six lectures. He had delivered one such series when he himself was delivered: A friend obtained for him an invitation to preach to a congregation at Nantwich, in Cheshire. He promptly accepted.

His three years at Nantwich were far happier in all respects than those at Needham Market had been. The new congregation was even smaller than his first but (in contrast with Needham Market's) was made up of "a good-natured friendly people" who took no exception to his unorthodox theology. His income, moreover, greatly increased, largely as a result of his success as a schoolmaster and private tutor on the side. He was enabled to buy some "scientifical" instruments with which to gratify his "taste for science"—"a small air pump, an electric machine, etc."—although he had in Nantwich no time in which to conduct original researches. He seems to have used his equipment largely in scientific demonstrations for the amusement of his students and their parents, thus greatly enhancing the reputation of his school. He also learned to play the flute. He boarded with a grocer, named John Eddowes, who introduced him to the instrument as "the easiest" of all musical instruments to play, and "though I was never a proficient in it, my playing contributed . . . to my amusement many years of my life." He thereafter strongly recommended "the knowledge and practice of music to all studious persons and it will be better for them if, like myself, they should have no very fine ear nor exquisite taste, as by this means they will be more easily pleased and be less apt to be offended when the performances they hear are but indifferent."

Then, in 1760, recommended by his Nantwich success as a teacher, he was offered the post of tutor in languages, classical and "polite," at a newly established Dissenter Academy in Warrington. His Nantwich school "promised to be more gainful" than the 100 pounds a year, plus possible private tutorial fees, which Warrington offered. Moreover, he wrote, "I should have preferred the office of teaching the Mathematics and Natural Philosophy, for which I had at that time a great predilection." Nevertheless, he accepted because it appeared to him that the Academy post "would be more liberal and less painful" than his present occupation. He entered on his new duties in September, 1761, and at once found that Warrington was in every respect a greater advance over Nantwich for him than Nantwich had been over Needham Market. During the six happy years that Priestley was part of it, the Academy was a major center of England's intellectual life, its faculty comprising as distinguished a group of scholars and thinkers as could be found in any educational institution in the country. There, where Unitarian theology was in process of being shaped out of Presbyterian free thought, Priestley's religious liberalism enhanced, rather than diminished, his social acceptability. There he was encouraged to pursue the scientific interests that had been first aroused in him at Daventry and further developed in Nantwich. There he met and married, on June 23, 1762, Mary Wilkinson, daughter of John Wilkinson, owner of a prosperous ironworks at nearby Wrexham and one of the leading figures in the Industrial Revolution then being initiated in England.

The marriage was happy. Priestley described his wife as "a woman of excellent understanding, much improved by reading, of great fortitude and strength of character, and of a temper in the highest degree affectionate and generous; feeling strongly for others, and little for herself." He further praised her as "greatly excelling in everything relating to household affairs." Others, describing her, stressed her sense of humor (her letters have been called "brighter" than her husband's), and she seems to have been much amused, now and again, by the foibles of her earnest, if sprightly and lively, husband. Marital bliss, however, imposed new obligations: A daughter was soon born to the Priestleys and, with her, the need for a larger income than that which Warrington afforded.

Largely in anticipation of this probability, Priestley, a month before his wedding, sought and obtained full ordination as a Dissenter minister. At the time he frankly confessed in a letter to a friend that his motive was economic:

> As all things in this world are uncertain, I think it a point of prudence not to omit anything that may possibly be of advantage to me, if ever it be my lot to be obliged to have recourse to the ministry for the whole or any part of my subsistence, particularly as I am going to have a

dearer and more important stake in this world than I have ever yet had in it. . . . The hazard of bringing a person into difficulties which she cannot possibly have any idea or prospect of affects me, at times, very sensibly.

In part from this same motive, he worked hard in Warrington to overcome his speech defect. He made a practice of reading aloud very slowly every day; he engaged in other speech exercises; he preached often from a Warrington pulpit, although this was no part of his required duties; and even though his stammer continued to plague him on occasion all his life, its frequency and severity were much reduced.

Thus, in 1767, when a call came to him from the Mill Hill Chapel, in Leeds, he was far better prepared to accept it than he had been to accept those at Needham Market and Nantwich. He left Warrington for Leeds in September, and his arrival was in the nature of a homecoming. Fieldhead, his birthplace, was a bare half-dozen miles from Mill Hill; the cloth market, where Jonas Priestley had sold his homespun, was but a mile or so away; and on every hand were familiar faces, friendly acquaintances of earlier years. His ministry was a success at the outset and continued this way through the six productive years that he remained in this pulpit. By the time he left Leeds, in 1773, he had become one of the best known and most controversial of England's public men, having contributed importantly to such various fields as education, theology, political economy, history, and physical science.

The Budding Scientist

Characteristic of Priestley was his likening of his troublesome speech impediment to Saint Paul's "thorn in the flesh" because "it has not been without its use." For instance: "Without some such check as this, I might have been disputatious in company, or might have been seduced by the love of popular applause as a preacher: whereas my conversation and my delivery in the pulpit having nothing in them that is generally striking, I hope I have been attentive to qualifications of a superior kind."

However that may have been, the "thorn" helped drive him into a greater reliance on literary composition, for self-expression, than he would otherwise have had. In marked contrast with his stammering speech was his facility as a rapid writer, a facility aided by his early mastery of a system of shorthand devised by Peter Annet. While yet a student at the Daventry Academy, Priestley composed the first draft of a theological work, *Institutes of Natural and Revealed Religion* (not published in its final revised form until 1768), initiating a voluminous stream of writings, which continued even to his deathbed. In 1761, his first year at Warrington, he published an *English Grammar,* which was originally composed for use in his Nantwich school and which had a marked success, going through several printings. David Hume (1711-76) acknowledged that he learned from it. In 1764 Priestley published an *Essay on a Course of Liberal Education for Civil and Active Life,* which provoked a storm of controversy because, highly critical of current educational practices, it insisted that the main object of education is to prepare the young to live in the current, actually existent world. If it made enemies, however, it also made important friends, among them Josiah Wedgwood, whose hugely successful pottery works epitomized the development of technology (and art) out of science whereby the Industrial Revolution was made. While at Warrington, Priestley also published an ingenious *Chart of Biography,* wherein—perhaps in emulation of the kind of induction Bacon had preached, certainly with usefulness to historians—he revealed at a glance by means of lines and spaces the temporal order in which the great men of every age and profession had lived and the relative lengths of their lives. For this production the author was awarded an honorary degree of doctor of laws by the University of Edinburgh.

Also at Warrington, he composed *Lectures on History and General Policy,* delivering them with great effect on his hearers; the work was not published until 1788, after he had revised and expanded it. In 1768, a year after his removal to Leeds, he published an *Essay on Government,* which—although no longer read—is of some importance to intellectual history because from it the English philosopher Jeremy Bentham (1748-1833) obtained the essential idea of what became known in philosophy as Utilitarianism. Following the lead of John Locke and the Scottish philosopher Francis Hutcheson (1694-1746), Priestley wrote that "the good and happiness of the members, that is, the majority of the members of any state, is the great standard by which everything relating to that state must be finally determined." Young Bentham was thereby led to the over-hasty conclusion that "goodness" and "happiness"—or "pleasure" (he dubiously deemed happiness and pleasure to be the same)—are synonymous; that "pain" and "evil" are synonymous; and that, therefore, the ethical value of any act can be given a statistical definition in terms of "the greatest good [happiness, pleasure] of the greatest number."

Soon after moving to Leeds, Priestley inaugurated a magazine, *The Theological Repository,* which was "meant to be a common channel of communication, which shall be open for the reception of all new observations that relate to theology." It provoked a good deal of theological controversy, but not enough subscriptions to meet its expenses. Priestley, who paid for much of its loss out of his own pocket, by no means a rich one, was forced to suspend the publication after three years. He also, in Leeds, engaged in intense political controversies involving the separation of Church and State and the freedoms of speech and press, which he, of course, strongly favored. In 1769, when the House of Commons refused to seat John Wilkes —who had been duly elected from Middlesex—because a majority hated his opinions, disapproved of his dissolute private character, and feared his demagoguery, Priestley made what he told a friend was "a bolder push than ever for the *pillory,* the *King's Bench Prison,* or something worse" by publishing a pamphlet supporting Wilkes and liberty.

But history's principal concern during this period results from his scientific work, of which he had done a good deal by the time he left Leeds. While he had been a lonely, obscure, and poverty-striken preacher in Needham Market, he had paid his first visit to London, a journey for which his "thorn in the flesh" was directly responsible. Having read the advertisement of a certain Mr. Angier, who claimed that he would cure any speech defect upon payment of a twenty-guinea fee, Priestley had persuaded his Aunt Sarah to supply the fee and had taken himself off to the metropolis. Mr. Angier's performance fell far short of his promise—it made Priestley's stammer worse—but, while in London, he made friends with two clerical doctors, who obtained for him the occasional extra five pounds he then so desperately needed and who also introduced him to men engaged in scientific investigation. He evinced thereafter a more active interest in science, using any spare money he obtained in Nantwich to buy laboratory equipment.

Not until he moved to Warrington, however, did he inaugurate the custom of spending one month out of each year in London. With these visits he began and maintained the friendships most crucially important to his early scientific career. One of these friendships was with Richard Price (1723-91), who deserves a more prominent place in history than he customarily receives. A liberal theologian whose views differed from Priestley's and led to much friendly, stimulating controversy between the two men, Price was also a mathematician who applied his skill to a solution of insurance problems, laying the foundations of the actuarial science with *Observations on Reversionary Payments* (published in 1771). Interested in all branches of science, he numbered many "natural and experimental philosophers" among his friends. On politics, Price and Priestley were in close agreement. Both sided with the American Colonies in their growing disagreements with the government of George III; Price went so far, in *Civil Liberty,* as to advocate the Declaration of Independence, of which the pamphlet is sometimes said to have been a cause. Such shared political views helped cement a friendship that was in any case natural, even inevitable, between Priestley and Benjamin Franklin (1706-90).

Franklin was then in London as an agent of the Colonies in their efforts to obtain from Britain a redress of their grievances, notably that of "taxation without representation." His fame as a scientist had been secured a dozen years before, in Philadelphia, with his electrical experiments (the lightning rod he had invented was in use everywhere); he had been elected an honorary Fellow of the Royal Society of London; and he enthusiastically supported Priestley's proposed history of electrical research, summarizing the knowledge that had been obtained. He offered to secure for Priestley all the available literature on the subject. This was in 1765, and Priestley plunged into the new work with his customary energy, completing in less than a year *The History and Present State of Electricity,* which included original experiments and copperplate illustrations.

Among the original experiments, conducted with the electric machine Priestley had purchased at Nantwich, was one that proved charcoal to be an excellent conductor of electricity. A more important experiment led to the discovery of one of the fundamental laws of electricity. In this experiment Priestley electrified with his machine a hollow metallic sphere, noted that there was no charge on its inner surface, and noted too that when small light objects were placed inside it, they were unmoved by an electrical attraction or repulsion. "Assuming, from experimental results already familiar, that the charge would be uniformly distributed over the surface of the sphere, and remembering that Newton had shown that no gravitational force existed within a uniform hollow sphere of matter, Priestley argued by analogy that electrical force must obey the same law as gravitational force," wrote E. J. Holmyard.[6] "But the gravitational attraction between two bodies varies inversely as the square of the distance between them; hence, if the analogy is justified, the force of attraction or repulsion between two electrical charges is also inversely proportional to the square of the distance between them." This law of inverse squares, as applied to electric charges, was experimentally verified about eighteen years later by the French scientist Charles A. Coulomb (1736-1806), and it is now known as Coulomb's law.

The *History* fully justified Priestley's election as a Fellow of the Royal Society—an event that occurred on June 12, 1766—but it was found to be too difficult for ordinary readers. Accordingly, Priestley prepared a popularization of the book, entitled *A Familiar Introduction to the Study of Electricity* (published in 1768). There was a by-product of these two works. Unable to find anyone who could make the drawings he needed, Priestley perforce made them himself, learning in the process rules for rendering three-dimensional space accurately on a plane surface. He would have been greatly helped at the outset by a book setting forth this information in clear and simple language, but no such book had been published. He undertook to supply the deficiency with *A Familiar Introduction to the Theory and Practice of Perspective* (published in 1770), a work which was highly recommended by drawing masters, had a considerable sale, and continued to be used into the next century. Incidentally, the Preface to this work contains what is said to be the first printed reference to the use of India rubber as an eraser of lead-pencil marks.

Priestley now projected an extremely ambitious literary work—nothing less than a complete history of all branches of "experimental philosophy," in multiple volumes. He launched the enterprise with a two-volume *History of Discoveries Relating to Vision, Light, and Colours,* published by subscription (Franklin bought twenty copies) in 1772. The sale of the work failed to pay the cost of printing and binding, however, and Priestley was forced to abandon the remainder of his grandiose scheme. The event, nevertheless, was fortunate for him and for the progress of science since, as a result, he turned his major attention to the chemical experiments that were to make him famous.

There is some irony—also some significance for the general nature of scientific discovery—in the story of how Preacher Priestley first became actively interested in pneumatic chemistry—that is, the chemistry of "airs" or, as we now say, gases. He had no such interest prior to 1767. Up to that time his knowledge of chemistry was almost wholly limited to what he had derived from a course of lectures given at the Warrington Academy by Dr. Turner of Liverpool. Dr. Turner had certainly spoken of "fixed air" (carbon dioxide); he may have mentioned the fact that "fixed air" is expelled from effervescent mineral waters—is indeed the "principle" of their effervescence—and can be "reimbibed" by them. At any rate, Priestley was aware of this fact in 1767, for he mentions having read "Dr. [William] Brownrigg's excellent paper on the Spa water," a paper in which Brownrigg discussed the possibility of making a water having properties similar to those of Seltzer water. Great practical importance was attached to this subject at the time. Physicians sustained laymen in an exaggerated estimate of the medicinal value of the effervescent waters. For one thing, they believed such waters were effective in the treatment of scurvy.

The interest thus created in Priestley's mind might well have remained passive had he not happened to move into a house in Meadow Lane, next door to the brewery of Jakes and Nell, when he first came to Leeds. He confessed as much. "Had it not been for this circumstance," he frankly said, "I should, probably, never have attended to the subject of air at all."

As it was, he became interested in the possibility of impregnating ordinary water with the "fixed air" so copiously released from the brewery's fermentation vats. His first experiment consisted simply of placing (in his own words) "shallow vessels of water within the region of fixed air, on the surface of the fermenting vessels; and having left them all night, I generally found, the next morning, that the water had acquired a very sensible and pleasant impregnation." It then occurred to him that the process of impregnation might be speeded and its degree increased, "by pouring the water from one vessel into another, while they were both held within the sphere of fixed air; and accordingly I found that I could do as much in about five minutes in this way, as I had been able to do in many hours before."

There the matter stood in the summer of 1768, when he moved from Meadow Lane into a house on Basinghall Street, so far away from the brewery as to make visits there inconvenient. He therefore made no more of what he called "artificial Pyrmont water" until the spring of 1772, when he was stimulated into further experiments along this line by another "mere accident." He was dining with the Duke of Northumberland when "his Grace produced a bottle of water distilled by Dr. Irving for the use of the navy." The company drank it and found it, Priestley said, "perfectly sweet, but, like all distilled water . . . [it] wanted the briskness and spirit of fresh spring water." It immediately occurred to him that he could "easily mend that water for the use of the navy, and perhaps supply them with an easy and cheap method of preventing or curing sea scurvy, viz. by impregnating it with fixed air." The general method of doing so was by this time clear to him, for the interest in "air" that had been aroused continued active, leading him to perform increasingly sophisticated experiments with it. To obtain "fixed air," he now poured "oil of vitriol" (sulfuric acid) over coarsely powdered chalk (calcium carbonate) in a bottle. Into the neck of the bottle he inserted a cork with a tube running through it into a bladder. When all the "common" air had been driven out of the bladder, which was then inflated with "fixed air," he led the latter through a glass tube into a basin of water and through that into a bottle of water that had been inverted in it. The water in the bottle was quickly saturated.

By devising this simple method, Priestley became in effect the inventor of soda water and other effervescent beverages. He published his method at once in a pamphlet, entitled *Directions for Impregnating Water With Fixed Air*. He also demonstrated it before the College of Physicians, which recommended its use by the Navy, whereupon two British warships were equipped with the necessary apparatus. In part because of this and in part because of his other and (by present standards) more important early experiments on "air," whose results were published in the *Philosophical Transactions of the Royal Society* in 1772, Priestley received the Royal Society's coveted Copley Medal on St. Andrew's Day, 1773. Soon thereafter, Richard

Bewley, an apothecary friend of Priestley's, discovered that he could increase the absorption of "fixed air" by water if he added to the water a small amount of carbonate of soda, thus producing what was long known as "acidulous soda water," another direct ancestor of today's soda pop and sparkling waters.

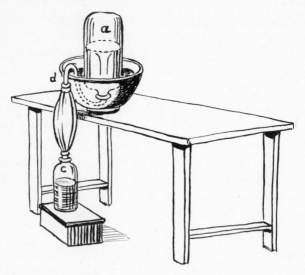

Priestley's apparatus for impregnating liquids with air. The air (gas) was produced in *c*.

Shelburne and Priestley

The year in which Priestley received the Copley Medal was also the year of his departure from Leeds. By then, his writings and experiments had brought him fame—and notoriety. They had not brought him a net profit, for he was constantly spending money for experimental apparatus and books and for the printing of his controversial pamphlets. Although his Mill Hill ministry provided him with a house to live in, his salary was a meager 105 pounds a year, and he had now a family of three children to support. Consequently, he was in straitened financial circumstances. This fact led his great and good elder friend Richard Price to recommend him strongly to Lord Shelburne, when the latter let it be known that he was looking for a librarian and literary companion, in the summer of 1772. The result was that Shelburne made Priestley an offer so handsome that he could not refuse it: a salary two and one-half times more than that paid him at Leeds; a large and pleasant house to live in during the summers at Calne, where Shelburne's estate, Bowood, was situated; another house, in London, for the winter months; and a life pension of 150 pounds a year in case the first connection between the two men should ever be dissolved. Moreover, his duties as librarian were to be light. He would have more free time to pursue his scientific and literary labors than he had ever had before. He moved to Calne in the early summer of 1773.

Of Priestley's patron, William Petty, the second Earl of Shelburne and later the first Marquess of Lansdowne, under whose patronage Priestley did nearly all the work for which he is remembered, Goldwin Smith wrote: "This man is an enigma." [7] Others have expressed the same opinion. Evidently one of the most intelligent men of his day, Petty was in his youth (and among his class) one of the most poorly educated. Some say that he was not far from illiterate when, in the late teens, he entered the Army. He served first under General James Wolfe, who years later triumphed over the French and was killed at Quebec; he distinguished himself in battle at Minden and Kloster-Kamp in Germany; and as a reward for his gallantry, he was made aide-de-camp to George III, who had then, in 1760, just come to the throne. In the following year, upon the death of his father, Petty succeeded to the Shelburne title.

As Lord Shelburne, he soon became one of England's leading political figures of the liberal wing. Under the ministry of George Grenville, who took office in 1763, he served as President of the Board of Trade briefly, resigning out of disagreement with Grenville's policies—especially his Colonial policy, which contributed heavily to the growth of American Revolutionary sentiment. Under the second ministry of the elder William Pitt, the Earl of Chatham, Shelburne was a Secretary of State, taking office in 1766. Soon afterward, Chatham fell ill. His mind was so seriously deranged that the country had in effect no Prime Minister for two years. Shelburne promptly found himself again in disagreement with his colleagues—especially on the American policy. He ceased attending Cabinet meetings and at last resigned his post in October, 1768. He was still out of office, living in retirement at Bowood, in 1773.

By this time Shelburne had gone far toward remedying the deficiencies of his early education. He had cultivated the friendship of the most brilliant men of his time, in England and on the Continent. His friends included Price, Sir William Blackstone (1723-80) the jurist and educational reformer, and Franklin. By picking their brains and by reading widely, he had become a man of culture, with a love of literature, an interest in science, and, of course, a very active interest in the theory and practice of government. "He seems highly enlightened for his day," wrote Goldwin Smith; "he is a sound economist and a pioneer of free trade. His policy toward America is liberal; he is against coercing her. . . . There appears to be much about him most excellent. Yet [and this is the enigma] he is intensely disliked and mistrusted. He is nicknamed Malagrida, after a Jesuit of sinister visage. By Burke he is compared to a serpent with two heads. Nobody cares to act with him." [8] Why? In recorded history there is no answer.

Evidently there was in him a personal coldness—an incapacity for love—which set at naught all his calculated
kindnesses and generosities. Even Priestley, who owed him
much and was one of the least malicious of men, could
not love him or long maintain with him any real quality
of friendship.

Joseph Priestley, when he moved to Calne and into the
period of his greatest work and fame, was forty years
old. He was of middle height (five feet, eight inches),
slender, well proportioned, and erect in posture. His hair
and complexion were fair, his eyes a clear gray, his lips
very thin, and his jaw was rather more than normally long
and firm. He seldom laughed but often smiled—rather
primly, without parting his lips or narrowing his rather
heavy-lidded eyes.[9] He was physically very neat and clean,
fastidiously so, and wholly without ostentation. He normally dressed in sober black and white—a high white stock,
a long black coat, a white powdered wig, and a black
cocked hat—when he appeared in public. He was a brisk,
seemingly tireless walker, habitually carrying a long cane,
and indeed was very quick and precise in all his bodily
movements. He had in general the appearance of the
stereotyped country parson or schoolmaster of English
drama and fiction—a benign, abstracted figure, abstemious
and dignified, methodical and self-contained, and so firmly
in control of his passions as to seem not to have them.

Nor did his appearance belie his mental character and
habits of life. Early to bed and early to rise, he was concerned to spend each day and every hour of each day as
economically as possible. He was helped to do so by a shorthand diary, in which he noted the chief events of his day,
the books he had read, the work he was engaged in, the
ideas he had for future work, and (always) the precise
hours of his arising and going to bed. The diary was not

only a record of personal history but also a yardstick for measuring his performance. It was one of several; he was very much a creature of work plans and timetables. At the beginning of each year he prepared a general schedule of activities, with particular emphasis on the work to be completed in the coming twelvemonth; at the end of each he measured his accomplishments against it, noting where he had exceeded and where he had fallen short of his expectations. This large plan was not his only one. Within its framework was a multitude of smaller schedules. Whenever he started to read a book, he noted, at least in his mind, the time at which he should complete it. He did the same with every activity. By this precise allocation of time he was enabled to shift painlessly from one activity to another and to apply himself industriously to each within the block of time allotted to it, in consequence of which— and because he was a naturally fast worker—the quantity of his completed labors grew prodigiously.

All this bespeaks great willpower, disciplining great mental and physical energy; it also bespeaks certain mental deficiencies. Priestley later spoke of his "most humbling failure of recollection" and went on to make it clear that this "failure" had nothing to do with the kind of absent-mindedness which, being the result of a complete absorption in abstract ideas, often characterizes genius. (It notably characterized Isaac Newton.) He wrote, ruefully: "I have so completely forgotten what I myself have published, that in reading my own writings what I find in them often appears perfectly new to me, and I have more than once made experiments the results of which have been published by me." He would not have forgotten work that was in the highest degree creative; no one who has suffered the gestation period and birth pangs of concepts wholly his own, of works wholly new and individual in the world, can forget them ever. Nor would he have been so dependent on schedules if he had had the ability to concentrate intensely for long periods of time on a single subject— an ability outstandingly characteristic of Kepler, Galileo, and Newton, the three giants of the preceding century. A mind as confined by schedules as Priestley's is likely to gain in efficiency at the expense of inspiration; it must often reject insights and intuitions whose objective realization would throw all work plans and all time schemes awry.

But if these be defects, they may be necessary to the kind of mental virtues Priestley abundantly possessed. His historic role at Calne was to be the accumulation of the raw materials, the "brute facts," out of which a man very different from him in character and mentality was to shape a new revolutionary theory, after he had destroyed a false theory that, in 1773, remained a major obstacle to scientific progress. The name of this man, who was already well known when Priestley assumed his duties at Bowood, was Antoine Lavoisier.

2. Antoine Lavoisier:
The Making of a Scientist

The Lavoisier Family

Antoine Laurent Lavoisier was born in Paris, in a small mansion in the Cul-de-sac Pecquet, on the morning of Monday, August 26, 1743, and was christened at three o'clock that afternoon in the ancient parish Church of St.-Merry. He was the fifth male to be named Antoine in seven generations of his family.

The family had been climbing the social and economic ladder, slowly but steadily, for a century and a half by 1743, when it had reached a place in the upper middle class only one rung below the nobility. The earliest Antoine Lavoisier of whom there is a definite record began the climb. The son of a peasant who wore out his life on a narrow plot of land near the village and forest of Villers-Cotterêts, about fifty miles east of Paris, during the second half of the sixteenth century, the first Antoine became skilled in the handling of horses and managed in this capacity to attract the attention of the king's entourage—

perhaps the attention of the king himself—when the royal huntsman (Louis XIII) came to kill wild boar and deer and hare in the local forest, which was his hunting preserve. This earliest Antoine became a postilion in the service of the king—that is, he rode the left lead horse of the four or six horses that customarily drew the royal carriage. He died in 1620, the year that English Puritan Dissenters landed from the *Mayflower* at Plymouth Rock, in New England.

His son, the second Antoine, raised in the postilion's quarters above the royal stables at Villers-Cotterêts, followed naturally enough in his father's footsteps. He too became a postilion. But while still a very young man, he was enabled greatly to improve his situation. His native village lay on the main highway between Paris and the Channel port of Calais; when the highway became a post road, near the turn of the century, young Antoine became the local postmaster—an office that had nothing to do with the mail, but everything to do with the care of horses and the management of the post facilities. It was in the posthouse at Villers-Cotterêts, therefore, that the third Antoine Lavoisier was born in 1606, the eldest of five children. Unlike his father and grandfather, this Antoine did not remain illiterate all his life—he was sent as a child to the village curé for education—and his literacy enabled him to become assistant to the sheriff of the district. In June, 1630, he made an advantageous marriage to Madelaine Dubois, the daughter of a local merchant.

Ten years later, in 1640, a child was born to them, a son whom (departing from the established pattern) they did *not* name Antoine. Instead, they had him christened Nicholas. Having learned reading, writing, and arithmetic as a boy, Nicholas went to work for the merchant Dubois, his maternal grandfather. Ultimately he established a small but prosperous mercantile business of his own, becoming the first of the Lavoisiers to accumulate an inheritance—although a modest one—for his children. He also became the first Lavoisier to marry a woman who had been raised outside his native countryside—a fact in evidence of his having more mobility and his knowing a wider world than his forebears. Barbe Lagonée was her name, the wedding took place in 1673, and five years later the couple had their first child, a son whom, returning to the earlier family pattern, they named Antoine. He was sent to law school. He returned to become the king's legal agent in the district of Villers-Cotterêts, as well as superintendent of the forest which, with the château, was now in possession of the Duc d'Orléans. In 1705 he married Jeanne Waroquier, daughter of a well-to-do lawyer of the neighboring district. After ten barren years (in this he duplicated the experience of his paternal grandfather), he became the father of a son, who was named Jean Antoine.

Then, during the first half of the eighteenth century, the Lavoisiers climbed through the upper ranks of the bourgeoisie to the very edge of the aristocracy. Jean Antoine was sent, aged sixteen, to law school—not to a provincial law school, as his father had been, but to the law school in Paris, where his record was excellent. Nor did he return to Villers-Cotterêts. His maternal uncle, Jacques Waroquier, a *procureur* (*i.e.*, magistrate) of the Parlement of Paris (the chief French judicial court), owned the small mansion in the Cul-de-sac Pecque where Antoine Laurent was to be born. There, just a short walk from the Palais de Justice, Jean Antoine made his home as a law student, and there he continued to live when he was appointed his uncle's assistant. He became the owner of the house in 1741, when his uncle died; he also inherited his uncle's modest fortune of some 40,000 livres; and climaxing his lucky chances, he was appointed to his uncle's place as *procureur*. He was thus, at twenty-six, in a position to make a good marriage, and he made an excellent one the next year.

His choice fell on the daughter of Sieur Clément Punctis, a man of considerable wealth, one of the most influential lawyers in Paris, and the secretary to the Marquis de Château-Renault, who was Vice Admiral of France. Her name was Émilie, and in her circumstances and with her charms (for she was considered a beauty) she might easily have married a title. Instead, on June 5, 1742, with her father's blessing (which speaks well for the attractiveness and promise of Jean Antoine) she became Mme. Lavoisier, adding to her husband's growing fortune a dowry of some 17,000 livres. A little more than a year later she became the mother of the fifth Antoine Lavoisier, who was destined to be the last and by far the greatest of his line.

The fifth Antoine was also destined to epitomize the dominant characteristics of the family as they had developed or had been revealed since the first Antoine began the family's rise—characteristics, for the most part, of the French bourgeoisie. The Lavoisiers were evidently a shrewd, calculating, hardheaded people. Strongly driven by worldly ambition and with the acquisitive instinct very much alive in them, they had an eye for the main chance and were quick to seize it. Matters of religion and conscience evidently played no such part in the life of any Lavoisier as that which they played in the life of every Priestley. Conservative in all things—especially in the expenditure of emotional energy—they held orthodox religious views while avoiding the kind of "enthusiasm" so deplored by Locke at the close of a long century of bloody conflict between Protestant and Catholic. They were of a superior general intelligence, they were industrious, and they had great willpower and self-discipline; but there is no evidence of their being notably generous or warmhearted. On the other hand, there is some evidence of a certain coldness in them, an arrogance which intensified their family loyalty while rendering it quite rigorously exclusive. From one point of view this was a weakness of moral character, but it was to be more than compensated for in the last generation by an all-absorbing commitment to an ideal and to a system of creative ideas whose practical realization has been an immense boon to mankind.

A *Privileged Youth*

Between Antoine Laurent Lavoisier's boyhood in Paris and that of Joseph Priestley in Yorkshire there were few points of similarity, but one of them was important to the development of their very different characters. Both lost their mothers at an early age; both were raised by aunts who had no children of their own.

In 1745 Antoine's mother gave birth to a daughter, who was christened Marie Marguerite Émilie. She never recovered her health afterward. She died in 1748, when Antoine was five, becoming thereafter to her son, as Joseph Priestley's mother had become to him, a vague dreamlike figure out of an almost forgotten past. The death of her distinguished father, Sieur Clément Punctis, occurred within a few months of her own. The widower, Jean Antoine Lavoisier, then moved with his two children from the small mansion in the Cul-de-sac Pecquet into the much larger mansion of the widowed Mme. Frère Punctis in the Rue du Four St.-Eustache (now the Rue de Vauvilliers). The upbringing of his two motherless children was undertaken by the dead Émilie's younger sister, Antoine's Aunt Constance, who became every bit as beloved by her nephew as was Aunt Sarah by Joseph Priestley. She devoted her life utterly to her sister's children, refusing (it is said) several offers of marriage. Antoine's boyhood, in consequence, was settled and happy. He was the object of the kind of love that develops emotional security—a confidence in one's own worth and a certainty about one's valued place in the world. Moreover, his economic circumstances were the best. Unlike Joseph Priestley, Antoine Lavoisier would never know from personal experience, as boy or as man, what it meant to be poor.

Yet poverty of the most miserable, soul-destroying kind was all around him in the Paris of Louis XV, in which he grew to maturity. Even as a child, he could not wholly avoid the sights and sounds and smells of it. One of his biographers, Sidney J. French, pictured him clinging to his father's cloak in shrinking fear of the wretched children who mocked him, as the Lavoisiers, father and son, homeward-bound from the heart of the city, walked past the Place de Grèves and through the filthy, narrow, crooked streets of the Paris slum.[1] In 1750, when he was seven, riots raged through the wintry streets of Paris for a long week. Whether or not they aroused in him a deep personal sympathy for the oppressed is questionable: The ragged, dirty, hollow-eyed creatures, their faces distorted by hate and suffering, appeared more bestial than human. They were a dangerous rabble; they must be kept under control.

Grinding poverty was also unavoidably witnessed whenever he was taken, as he was each year, for extended visits with relatives in Villers-Cotterêts. The peasants of France were beasts of burden, living far less well than the dogs and horses of the nobility. Using inefficient tools and antiquated methods, they struggled to wrest family livings from a few acres of unfertilized soil, and of their meager cash income (it has been estimated to have averaged no more than 100 livres annually per family) they were required to pay out more than 80 percent in direct taxes and a substantial portion of the remainder in indirect taxes. "It seems incredible that the peasants survived at all, under such ruthless extortion," wrote Gaetano Salvemini in *The*

French Revolution.[2] They were not permitted to fence their cropland where such fences might interfere with the cross-country sport of aristocratic huntsmen; if they were caught poaching in the numerous and extensive hunting parks, they were cruelly executed. The hovels they lived in had dirt floors and no windows. They ate the coarsest food, which rarely included meat or wine, and were continuously at the edge of starvation. Often they were pushed over the edge by bad harvests. Oftener still they died of epidemic disease.

There was talk in Antoine's boyhood home about the deplorable financial condition of France and about the need for financial reform. Much of it concerned the Parlement of Paris, where Jean Antoine continued to serve as a magistrate. The Parlement not only was a supreme judicial body but also had the function of "registering" (that is, publishing and promulgating) royal decrees, a function which in practice had come to involve the right to criticize the edicts submitted to it and even, on occasion, to refuse to register them. The king might then enforce the registration by calling the Parlement into a special session, known as the *lit de justice,* although this naked display of monarchical power was not without risks for the Crown in such times of economic distress and popular unrest as those that prevailed all through the reign of Louis XV. They were risks the king was often reluctant to run. Thus, both Crown and Parlement had weapons to use against each other, and they used them in continuous strife while Louis XV was on the throne until at last, in 1770, he felt driven to the dangerous extreme of abolishing the Parlement of Paris and banishing 150 magistrates from the city. It was then reconstituted with new members and on a new basis.

But those who sided with the Parlement in this strife were not on that account siding with liberty and progress against repression and reaction. As a political institution, the Parlement was reactionary. Through it the nobility and higher clergy sought to force a weak, mistress-dominated Louis XV to restore to them feudal powers they had lost to the Crown under Louis XIV. Such success as they had in this enterprise weakened the power of the central government to effect desperately needed reforms—reforms which would reduce their privileges and which most of them therefore stubbornly opposed. Nor was the Parlement any better as a final court of justice. On the contrary, it was notoriously inefficient, corrupt, inhumane, and intolerant, as the great Voltaire (1694-1778) repeatedly and angrily charged. The consequences of its acts and of its failures to act were all too frequently horrible in that age and land of barbarous punishments.

Consider, for example, one not untypical case that came to Voltaire's attention; it throws light on that "justice" of the Old Regime that made the regime a continuous reign of terror for common folk. On a highway in Lorraine, one morning in 1769, a man was found robbed and murdered. Someone said the victim had taken a jacket from a peasant, named Martin. This was deemed a sufficient motive for the crime, and Martin, a very poor and ignorant man, was arrested. He protested his innocence, claiming he had been sound asleep with his family when the crime was committed. None of the stolen money was found in his possession. None of his family or neighbors was questioned. Nevertheless, he was tortured, briefly tried, and quickly condemned to suffer death on the wheel. The Parlement of Paris, called on to review the case, did so in the most perfunctory manner, if at all, before it confirmed the sentence, which was then immediately carried out. Not long afterward a condemned criminal confessed that he had done the murder for which Martin had died. And what was the form of poor Martin's death? It was then a common form of execution in France. Let Georg Brandes describe it:

> He [the condemned] was tied face-outward on a St. Andrew's cross, and laid on the scaffold. Over niches in the cross lay the extremities that were to be broken with an iron rod by the executioner. Next came a few blows on the chest. The executioner's art consisted in keeping the criminal alive as long as possible. . . . The body was tied to a coach wheel in such a way that the toes touched the the back of the head. . . . [T]he poor wretch who was unfortunate enough to remain alive on the wheel as long as two days and two nights was strangled in some cases. . . . If . . . [the French people] showed cruelty in the [French Revolution's] Reign of Terror, it was because they had learned it from the autocracy, and it was mild in comparison with that of the Monarchy.[3]

Of at least one of the major quarrels between Parlement and King, young Antoine heard a great deal when, in his teens, he became a regular member of his grandmother's salon. The Parisian salon of the eighteenth century was a unique institution, whose importance extended far beyond that of mere social recreation. It developed conversation into a fine art; it refined manners; it elevated formal aesthetic tastes (if at a substantial cost in terms of spontaneity and sincerity); and in a country where the freedoms of press and public speech were severely limited, it provided one of the few means of shaping and informing a public opinion. Salon society was small, but it included nearly all the truly influential, a fact giving historical importance to such glittering rival salons as Mme. Geoffrin's and Mme. du Deffand's. No such importance was attached to the salon of Mme. Frère Punctis. It was very small, intimate, excessively earnest by prevailing salon standards, and wholly unknown to fame. Nevertheless, it numbered among its most faithful and regular attendants a famous man, whose influence on young Antoine was of decisive importance. His name was Jacques Étienne Guettard (1715-86).

Guettard, who had been raised and educated by Jesuit fathers, was passionately committed to the Jesuit order. Most Frenchmen were passionately hostile to it, on political more than on theological grounds. Especially was this true in the bourgeoisie, where Jansenism (Catholic Puritanism) flourished despite a papal bull branding the teachings of Cornelis Jansen (1585-1638) as heretical. Thus, in 1762, when Jansenists dominated the Parlement of Paris, they ordered the confiscation of all Jesuit property devoted to worldly use. Two years later, in November, 1764, a royal edict, issued under pressure from the Parlement, expelled the Jesuits from France. Guettard was embittered. He missed no opportunity, favorable or unfavorable, to defend his beloved order with a vehemence that bordered on violence.

But it was not Guettard the angry polemicist who profoundly influenced Antoine. It was Guettard in his total character as a man and in his role as a scientist. He was a crusty old bachelor, strongly opinionated, set in his ways, and inclined to identify politeness with hypocrisy and harshness of manner with honesty. He made a fetish of brutal frankness and so made many personal enemies. Yet, as with many people of his type, his crustiness was a protective armor for feelings that, in his bachelor's loneliness, were more easily hurt than most men's. If he was contemptuously indifferent to the kind of affection that is widely but thinly spread and goes by the name of "popularity," he craved and was able to give a rare warmth and depth of friendship in his relationships with the few for whom he cared. He was an absolutely dedicated scientist, who had become a distinguished botanist before turning his attention to geology, a science he helped found. He was a member of the French Academy of Science. He was also curator of the natural history museum established in the Palais Royal by the Duc d'Orléans.

Young Antoine spent many hours in the museum with Guettard and many more on geological expeditions with him into the country around Paris. They studied rock formations, they collected rock samples, they examined the waters of springs and streams, and the boy listened with fascination to the man's plan for making a "mineralogical" (geological) atlas of all France, a task analogous in scope and difficulty to the exploration of a newly discovered continent since no geological map then existed. As for the crusty Guettard, he came to love Antoine as a son of whom he was very proud and for whom he had high ambitions. He recognized brilliant talents in the youth and was eager to enlist them in the service of science.

But in France, even more than in the England of those days, science was not a profession but an avocation, pursued in such hours as were free from duty. Jean Antoine Lavoisier stressed this fact in conversations with his son, while the latter, in his mid-teens, studied in Paris' Collège Mazarin. (The college had been founded by Cardinal Mazarin, Prime Minister under Louis XIV.) The father urged on his son the advantages of the law as a profession; it was agreed that Antoine would enter the Paris law school when his college studies were completed.

In any case, the achievement of scientific fame was not Antoine's chief personal ambition at this time. At the Collège Mazarin he began to study mathematics under Abbé Nicholas Louis de Lacaille (1713-62), who had an astronomical observatory attached to the college. He attended other scientific lectures whenever he could. But his principal aspiration was for literary distinction—an aspiration encouraged by the college's curriculum. He wrote drama, but significantly, it was in the essay and on a topic related to science that he won his only recorded literary success. At the Sorbonne, when he was seventeen, he won second prize in a general competition for an essay on the topic "Is uprightness as essential as accuracy in research?" How he answered the question is unknown; the essay has been lost.

This was in 1760. In the same year he suffered a great personal tragedy. His beloved sister, Émilie, died. He was for a time overwhelmed by grief, and it was perhaps a partial consequence that his late adolescence and early manhood were marked by a tenseness of spirit, a seriousness of purpose unusual in one of his years and social position.

An Education in Science and the Law

Certainly the regimen he imposed on himself was severe when, aged eighteen, he entered the Paris law school. He carried two burdens, either of them heavy enough to test the strength of most young men. One consisted of his law-school studies; they were rigorous, and although his heart was not in them, he was determined to do well in them for his father's sake. The other consisted of his scientific studies, to which he devoted a whole heart and all he could give of his time and energy. He hoarded the last jealously in order to commit them to his purposes from early each morning until late each night. He cut himself off from all social recreations. He denied himself to his friends, giving ill health as his excuse. Indeed, the excuse may have become a valid one under the continuous strain he imposed on himself: For some months he lived on an exclusive diet of milk. More awesome than endearing was his display of driving ambition and willpower, and it moved one of his worried and exasperated friends to send him a bowl of gruel with a note saying, "One year on earth is worth more than a hundred in the memory of men." If the implied advice had any modifying effect on Antoine's regimen, there is no evidence of it.

Under the Abbé de Lacaille he continued to study astronomy and mathematics (he mastered the calculus invented by Newton and Leibniz) until the Abbé died when Antoine was nineteen. He studied botany and zoology at the Jardin du Roi under the academician Bernard de Jussieu (1699-1777). From Guettard he took formal courses in geology and mineralogy. He studied anatomy and meteorology; the latter particularly fascinated him. He purchased a barometer, a thermometer, and a rain gauge. He began to take barometric and temperature readings several times each day, writing them down in a leather-backed notebook, in which he also recorded precipitation figures. He established a regular correspondence with men whom he persuaded to undertake similar observations elsewhere, thus establishing what are now called weather stations not only in various parts of France but also in places as distant as Baghdad. He continued this active interest into the last months of his life, his belief or hope being that there would emerge from the masses of data thus accumulated a definite pattern whereby rules of weather prediction could be devised. (In 1790 he suggested the daily publication of weather forecasts.) More important than this, in view of his future work, were the lectures on chemistry he attended at the Jardin des Plantes. These were delivered by the academician Guillaume François Rouelle (1703-70), a great teacher and lovable eccentric, whose influence on Lavoisier's mind was profound and lasting. It was through Rouelle that he was introduced to the phlogiston theory of combustion that was to loom so large in his later life, and it was in Rouelle's private laboratory that he first stained his hands with chemicals as he repeated primitive experiments.

Simultaneously he completed on schedule his law-school courses. He became a bachelor of laws in 1763 and a licentiate in 1764. He was thus formally prepared to step into the place his father held open for him in the Parlement of Paris. But he was not prepared by natural inclination to do so. On the contrary, he was by this time determined *never* to practice law if he could avoid it, and he was enabled honorably to avoid it in the very year that he received his license to practice.

His savior was his old friend Guettard, who had launched his ambitious project for mapping France mineralogically and had found, as he neared his fiftieth year, that he could not possibly complete the task unaided. He had been encouraged to hope for a grant from the government to finance his work, but none had yet been given. Meanwhile, he desperately needed an assistant of superior abilities, who could or would work for nominal pay. His natural first choice was Antoine Lavoisier, and the twenty-year-old Antoine joyfully accepted the offer. For the next three years, from 1763 to 1766, his major activity was the collection of data Guettard needed, usually in Guettard's company—data he later worked over in the Punctis mansion or in Villers-Cotterêts, where he continued to spend his vacations with relatives. The two men concentrated their efforts in the Île-de-France, as the region around Paris was called, accumulating masses of facts about rocks, soils, fossils, minerals, and water supplies. When the Île-de-France work was completed, there was a lull in this activity until 1767, when Guettard at last received the official patronage he had sought: The government agreed to finance the mineralogical atlas, specifying that he begin by mapping Alsace and Lorraine. He asked Lavoisier to collaborate with him, and Lavoisier, then twenty-four, accepted.

Meanwhile, Lavoisier had continued to exercise the iron

will and disciplined energy he had first displayed in law
school. His social life remained meager as he continued to
bear a double burden, that of his assigned work with Guettard and that of his own creative work.

In 1764 he engaged in his earliest known original research, a study of the mineral gypsum. When gypsum is
carefully heated to a temperature of about 125 degrees
Fahrenheit, it becomes a fine white powder, whose essential composition is now known to be hydrated calcium
sulfate ($CaSO_4$). The addition of water transforms the
powder into a plastic mass, which quickly hardens, or sets,
expanding slightly as it does. These properties make the
substance uniquely valuable for the making of casts, for
stuccowork, and for the finishing coats on plastered walls,
and it had become known as plaster of Paris because it
was so widely used in Parisian buildings. But what actually happened when gypsum was heated and water was
added to the resultant powder? *Why* (in the scientific sense,
meaning *how*) did the heated gypsum become powder?
Why did the plaster set? The very simple experiment devised by Lavoisier to answer these questions became, in
one essential respect, the pattern of all the great work
of his later years. The assumption of the perfect balance between material forces (the sense of an "equality of
oppositions") which permeates Newton's physics—a way
of thinking doubtless encouraged in Lavoisier by his law-
school training, with its emphasis on "justice"—had evidently become so deeply ingrained in the youthful Frenchman that he applied it as if by instinct to the problem now
before him. He very carefully weighed his samples of gypsum before heating them, he weighed the powders afterward, and he weighed the hardened plasters formed by the
addition of water. Discovering that water was lost from
the gypsum during the initial heating, he calculated the
amount lost and found that it precisely equaled the

amount that recombined with the powder to form a hardened plaster. He concluded that the process by which the plaster set was one whereby, through a recombination with water, the crystalline structure of the original gypsum was regained.

The paper in which he reported this to the Academy of Science in 1765, when he was twenty-two, was the least important to science of the dozens of papers, many of them classics, which he was to submit before he died. Nevertheless, it is significant to the historian and biographer on three counts. The *first count* concerns method: It impressed on chemistry a habit of precise quantitative measurement that had not formerly characterized it. The *second count* concerns the "proper attitude" of the experimental scientist: Lavoisier insisted that the chemist reporting his experiments confine himself to demonstrated facts and avoid speculations. For instance, it had long been known that an overheated gypsum would not bind with water to form a hardened plaster, and Lavoisier had noted this fact; but although he believed he could guess its cause, he refused in his report to do so, saying that such guessing was out of place in a science that could advance only through exact experiment. The *third count* has to do with a personal characteristic of Lavoisier's which later would involve him in difficulties: He was loath to acknowledge his debts to the work of others. In 1759, six years before Lavoisier's *The Analysis of Gypsum,* there had appeared a French translation of a work on the same subject, reaching the same general conclusions, by the German chemist Andreas Sigismund Marggraf (1709-82), chiefly remembered today as the discoverer of beetroot sugar, but also important for the improvements he made in the methods of qualitative chemical analysis. A preliminary "review of the literature" was by then already an established practice for the researcher, but no mention of Marggraf is made in Lavoisier's paper.

In the same year, 1765, the government of Paris offered through the Academy a prize of 2,000 livres for an essay on the best means of lighting city streets at night. Lavoisier entered the competition. He studied all the kinds of lamps then available, those burning oil, as well as those burning candles. He calculated the relative efficiencies of different oils, of wicks having various shapes, of elliptical and hyperbolic reflectors, and of different light standards. He estimated the costs of installation and maintenance and even made suggestions for financing the project. He failed to win the prize—it was divided among three other contestants (one of whom, Jean Sylvain Bailly, became a good friend of Lavoisier's)—but his paper displayed such mastery of the theoretical aspects—the physics and the mathematics—of the lighting problem that the Academy chose it for a signal honor. In a public ceremony on the evening of August 20, 1766, in the Academy's impressive quarters in the Louvre, its president, the elderly aristocrat Trudaine de Montigny, presented to the twenty-three-year-old Lavoisier a special gold medal "by order of the King." The event created something of a stir in Paris. Said the *Mercure de Paris* in its report: "The public views with pleasure the flattering distinction bestowed upon this young author, for which there is no precedent in the Academy of Science."

Mme. Frère Punctis died that year, 1766. Her estate, which was of a considerable size, was divided between her daughter, Constance, and her grandson, Antoine. The latter also received at this time about 200,000 livres from his father, Jean Antoine, who had exercised to good effect the typical Lavoisier shrewdness in money matters, multiplying through investments in land the small legacy left him by his uncle, Jacques Waroquier. All this was added to his sizable portion of his mother's estate with the result that, at twenty-three, two years before he had reached the legal age for Frenchmen, Antoine Lavoisier was financially independent. No urgent necessity to earn a living could henceforth interfere with the career in science he had launched so auspiciously.

On June 14, 1767, at three o'clock in the afternoon (such was the precision with which Lavoisier kept his diary), Guettard and his young assistant set out from Paris for their geological expedition to Alsace and Lorraine, accompanied by a family servant, named Joseph. They were on horseback—the condition of the roads where they were going would not permit their traveling in a wheeled vehicle—and Antoine's father and Aunt Constance were anxious for his safety. He had not before been separated for any length of time from his immediate family. In any case, some anxiety over so long a journey was justifiable in that day of abominable roads, which were infested by bandits, and wretched hostels, where bad food and filthy beds were the common rule. Guettard and Lavoisier carried pistols as a matter of course. So did Joseph.

Thanks to Antoine's diary and his almost daily letters home, we have an unusually full record of this expedition. He left detailed instructions with his father and aunt for the keeping of his weather records in Paris, instructions they precisely followed. He himself kept similar records all the while he was gone. Every morning between five and six o'clock, before they began their day's travel and work, he took readings from the barometer and thermometer he carried along with a hydrometer to measure water density and other scientific apparatus, in his closely packed saddlebags. He repeated the readings several times each day and never failed to take readings before he went to bed at night. He visited quarries, mines, ironworks, and bleaching works; invariably took temperature and density readings of the water of rivers he crossed, of mineral waters, and even of the water in the inns where he stayed; and paid particular attention to the kind of stone quarried and plaster used in the regions he visited.

At Basel, Switzerland, his barometer was accidentally broken, and Jacques Barière, an innkeeper otherwise unknown to history, insisted on presenting the expedition with the barometer he owned. At Strasbourg, in Alsace, Lavoisier spent 500 livres to purchase German books on chemistry that were at the time unavailable in Paris, and he apologized for his "extravagance" in a letter to his father. He also met two famous chemists, who no doubt encouraged the growth of the interest in chemistry which Rouelle's lectures in the Jardin des Plantes had aroused in him. One of them was F. L. Ehrmann. The other, J. R. Spielman, had just published a major work (it was one of the books Lavoisier bought), entitled *Institutiones chemiae* (brought out in Paris in 1770 as the *Instituts de chimie*). At Bourbonne-les-Bains Lavoisier was met by his father, who journeyed with the party to Chaumont, where he left to go to Villers-Cotterêts while Guettard and Antoine continued to Paris. In the evening of October 19, after an absence of a little more than four months, Antoine arrived safely at the Punctis mansion, where he was greeted with joyful relief by his Aunt Constance. He was very glad to be home again and very eager to lie again in a good bed, fatigued as he was by his journey. Nevertheless, he did not forget to take a barometric reading before he retired.

The work of the young Lavoisier as geologist was not destined to have a happy issue. Minister of Police Bertin, the principal official supporter of the atlas, had given insufficient consideration to financing its publication. The result was that all government money in support of the project had been used up by 1770, when only 16 of the proposed 230 sheets had been engraved. Lavoisier then suggested reducing the project to a total of 28 maps, to be completed in five years at a total cost of 40,000 livres, half of which would be supplied by private donors. He himself promised a generous donation. But at about this time the crusty Guettard's uncertain temper gave way under the pressure of frustrating delays and the hostility of powerful men whom he had personally offended. He presented a report to the Academy, in which he paid glowing tribute to the work of Antoine Lavoisier. Then, in anger, hurt, and disappointment, he abandoned his long-cherished dream. The atlas was finally published in incomplete form in 1780 by the government's Inspector General of Mines, Monnet, who ascribed its joint authorship to himself and Guettard, while using without credit the abundance of valuable data for whose collection Lavoisier alone was responsible. Lavoisier protested Monnet's "impudence," as he called it, and a lifelong enmity was developed between the two men.

Ambition

On June 1, 1768, about eight weeks before his twenty-fifth birthday, Antoine Lavoisier was formally admitted to membership in the French Academy of Science—the youngest by several years of the Academy's sixty-eight members. In those days the Academy's structure reflected the class structure of the nation as a whole. There was a hierarchy of membership, each grade having rights and privileges greater than those of the grades below it. At the top were twelve *honoraires,* chosen from the nobility; from this rank alone could be chosen the president and vice-president. Next came eighteen *pensionnaires;* they, along with the *honoraires,* were the only members permitted to vote on Academy affairs, and from among them might be chosen the director, the secretary, and the treasurer of the Academy. Next came twelve *associés* and then, the lowest grade, twelve *adjoints,* who had virtually no rights at all, save that of membership, and were relegated at Academy meetings to hard benches behind the chairs of the *associés.* Only as vacancies occurred in the higher ranks could an *adjoint* become an *associé* and an *associé* a *pensionnaire.* In addition to these fifty-four regular members, there were fourteen special members, listed as *associés libres, associés étrangers, pensionnaires vétérans,* and *associés vétérans.*

Lavoisier had been proposed for membership as early as 1766, but there was no vacancy to be filled until one Baron, a chemist, died in the spring of 1768. It then appeared certain that young Lavoisier—already personally and favorably known by most of the academicians and strongly backed by several of the most distinguished of them— would be appointed an *adjoint* by the king after having received a majority of the Academy's votes. A formidable rival now appeared, however. He was Gabriel Jars, a thirty-six-year-old metallurgist who had rendered many signal services to his country (for instance, he had introduced the manufacture of red lead into France), and he was strongly backed by the president of the Academy, a minister named De Saint-Florentine. Five other names, including Monnet's, were formally presented to the Academy on election day, which was May 18 that year, but the only serious competition was between Jars and Lavoisier, who was nominated by Lalande, the astronomer. Although Lavoisier received more votes than any other candidate in the balloting that followed, his margin over Jars was slender and in any case was not decisive. The Academy proposed, but the king disposed—and De Saint-Florentine, presenting the names of both Jars and Lavoisier to Louis XV, recommended Jars for the appointment. He was, however, respectful of the majority opinion of his colleagues in the Academy and accordingly further recommended a special arrangement whereby Lavoisier would be appointed an *adjoint,* increasing the membership by one above the legal sixty-eight, with the understanding that there would be no new election when the next vacancy occurred. This compromise the king accepted (his interest in the Academy and in science was very slight), and Lavoisier "won at his tender years an honor seldom attained under the age of fifty," to quote a letter received by Aunt Constance from a cousin of Antoine's. (Jars died a year later, and Lavoisier's membership was regularized.)

Election to the Academy was not the only crucial event in Antoine's life in the year 1768. When Lalande concluded his nominating speech, on May 18, he did so in the following words: "Monsieur Lavoisier is a young man of excellent repute, high intellect, and clear mind whose considerable fortune permits him to devote himself wholly to science." But if his "fortune" was "considerable," it was evidently not large enough to satisfy the ambitious young man. He had taken steps to increase it just two months before—steps that were regarded at the time as highly questionable on moral grounds by many of his scientific colleagues. (The latter were reassured by La Fontaine: "Ah, well! the dinners that he will give us will be all the better!") He had entered the *ferme générale,* the company of financiers who collected the king's taxes for him in the expectation—usually but not always fulfilled—of large profits. Each farmer-general, as the member was called, paid into the royal treasury the sum of 1,500,000 livres, purchasing with this the right to retain for himself such taxes as he could collect over a six-year period, at the end of which period he must renew his lease with the payment of another 1,500,000 livres. Antoine Lavoisier had only a third of the required amount to invest in March, 1768, but with it he purchased from a full-fledged farmer-general, named Baudon, a one-third interest in the lease of

Jean Alaterre. Lavoisier became a full-fledged farmer-general in 1780, a year after Baudon's death.

There were valid reasons for the loathing inspired in the masses by the farmers-general; Lavoisier's joining this enterprise has required apologetic explanations from his otherwise admiring biographers. In the preceding century the farmers-general had had the morals and manners of an American racketeer, extorting taxes by violence or the threat of violence from those least able to pay them, while flaunting their own wealth before the eyes of their victims. If the situation had somewhat improved during Louis XV's reign, it remained outrageous to acutely sensitive social consciences, and as one of Lavoisier's biographers put it, "[i]t is difficult to understand why Lavoisier chose to enter this nefarious organization." This biographer, Sidney J. French, went on:

> His social status as a farmer would certainly be no higher than that which he would have gained by entering his father's profession, or becoming a member of parlement. He knew the malodorous history of the tax farm,* since in his investigation of it he prepared a paper on its history. . . . It is reasonable to conclude that Lavoisier was prompted by no other motive than that which would give him considerable free time to devote to science. Yet, it was the most unfortunate step the young man ever took.[4]

Was it? Certainly it would seem so to a backward look, but at the time and long after, Lavoisier might count it one of the most fortunate steps he ever took. It greatly increased his wealth—he profited to the extent of nearly 1,200,000 livres from the *ferme* between 1768 and 1786, according to one careful estimate—and it led directly to his marriage, which proved to be singularly happy.

---

* *Farm* here refers to the *ferme générale*, whose members were called farmers or, officially, farmers-general.

He was assigned to the tobacco committee of the tax farm. The committee was headed by a very able administrator of wide culture and moderately liberal political views, named Jacques Paulze. From Paulze as a public administrator, the young Lavoisier evidently learned a great deal, and to the work of Paulze's committee he began at once to make valuable contributions: He was away from Paris for months at a time, examining tobacco warehouses, manufacturing plants, the watering of tobacco, and customs arrangements and in general collecting the factual information with which to support the proposals he was soon making for reforms of the *ferme's* operation. From Paulze as a social friend, he learned even more: In the brilliant Paulze salon, which he frequented, he met and mingled with France's liberal intellectual leaders, men strongly committed to the reform or abolition of antiquated social institutions. All these men were imbued with the spirit of the French *Encyclopédie,* the multivolumed work whose publication, begun in 1715, was called by André Billy "the greatest [event] . . . in the history of intellectual civilization since the invention of printing." [5]

Certainly the *Encyclopédie* was of prime importance. Its basic theme was that of Locke's philosophy (liberal France learned from England in those days); its articles emphasized over and over again that the facts of sense experience must be the final test of the validity of ideas; and as a whole it generated a mental climate of skepticism, materialism, and humanism that favored science while subverting the ancient authorities of Church and Crown. One of its later contributors, whom Lavoisier met in the Paulze salon, was the Marquis de Condorcet, whose lifespan was virtually identical with Lavoisier's (he was a month younger than Lavoisier; the two were to die in 1794) and whose temperament was evidently so similar to his as to make it difficult for the two to like each other, despite their great mutual respect. Condorcet, a brilliant mathematician, became a member of the Academy of Science in 1769. He might have come in as an *honoraire,* for he was of noble birth, but he preferred to enter as a working member. In this capacity he was destined to become, in 1777, the Academy's permanent secretary—not a very satisfactory one, in Lavoisier's view, since his interest in science lagged so far behind his interest in political economy that he neglected (charged Lavoisier) his official Academy duties.

Condorcet himself denied, in effect, any basis to the distinction between "science" and "political economy," for he was what is known as a "Physiocrat." So were the other key figures encountered by Lavoisier in the Paulze salon: Anne Robert Jacques Turgot; Pierre Samuel du Pont de Nemours, whose sons, in part as a consequence of his close friendship with Lavoisier, were to found in America the giant chemical firm of Du Pont de Nemours; Chrétien Guillaume de Lamoignon de Malesherbes, the jurist, who was to serve Louis XVI as minister and was to be one of the defense counsels when the king went on trial for his life before the National Convention in 1793; Trudaine de Montigny, tax reformer, academician, Director of Highways, and already a great friend and admirer of Lavoisier's; and Paulze himself. Lavoisier became essentially a Physiocrat insofar as he theorized at all in this field. What did the Physiocrats believe? As followers of François Quesnay (1694-1774) and as perfect specimens of the eighteenth-century rationalist, they believed there was an "inherent natural order" whereby society could and should be governed, the proper or just laws of society being of a piece with those that "govern" the physical world. To recognize this order and these laws was to recognize that land is the basis of all wealth, the ultimate source of all taxes, and that

unlimited freedom of industry and trade could alone ensure their "natural" development.

A growing interest in Physiocratic doctrine and the com-
panionship of brilliant men were not all that drew Lavoisier to the Paulze salon in 1770 and 1771. After the death
of Mme. Paulze in 1769, Jacques Paulze's hostess was his
daughter, Marie Anne Pierette. She was only thirteen when
her reign as hostess began, but mentally and physically she
was remarkably mature for her years. She was also remarkably attractive—a proud, slender, vivacious girl, whose eyes
sparkled with intelligence below level brows, who played
the harp and painted pictures with more than common
talent, and who displayed in conversation a quick wit and
an equally quick appreciation of the wit of others. Lavoisier was drawn to her. Easy to discern in the charming
child was the exciting woman she would become—a somewhat haughty beauty who would possess all the social
graces, as well as a precise mind joined to a strong will,
not unlike Lavoisier's own. He confessed to himself and
doubtless revealed in various ways to her and her father
that he wished her for his wife.

To the realization of this wish there was, at the outset,
a serious obstacle. Her mother's uncle was the powerful,
ruthless, and hated Abbé Terray, at the time Controller
General of Finance, who wished for personal political reasons to arrange a marriage between his grandniece Marie
and the Comte d'Amerval. The count had nothing to
recommend him to a young convent-educated girl, save his
title and a position in the highest society. He was fifty years
old, ugly, dissipated, and penniless (the probable size of
Marie's dowry was one of her chief attractions for him).
But he happened to be a favorite of the king's mistress,
Mme. du Barry, whose powerful support the Abbé Terray
then badly needed. Hence, the latter was furious when this
mere slip of a girl, Marie, put up a wrathful, tearful, stub-

born resistance to the proposal—and was sustained by her father. "I will not force her to marry a man to whom she has so decided an aversion!" said Paulze firmly. He risked much for his daughter's happiness and his own honor; it appeared certain for a time that the Abbé would carry out his threat to dismiss Paulze from the *ferme* in disgrace. But Paulze was not wholly defenseless, and the Abbé was pointedly reminded of this by one of Paulze's most influential colleagues in the *ferme,* who wrote: "M. Paulze is necessary to the *ferme*. He has instituted many needed reforms. . . . His loss would be a great blow. . . ." Terray was made to realize that the dismissal he contemplated might produce reactions dangerous to his own position; after all, if this position had been perfectly secure, if he had not felt the need for more support, he would not have proposed this marriage in the first place. He backed down.

Lavoisier at once proposed. The child-woman Marie had been constantly comparing the ugly old count with the handsome young scientist; the comparison had strengthened her determination never to become a d'Amerval. Lavoisier, now twenty-seven, was a handsome figure of a man. He was not especially robust—indeed his physical strength was not always equal to the strains he imposed on it—but he was tall (Marie at her tallest came barely to his shoulder) and beautifully proportioned, his well-shaped legs showing to advantage in the long hose and tight knee breeches which were the standard masculine attire in those days. He was handsome of face, too. It was an oval face, rather smaller than might be expected above a body of his size, its tall forehead framed (when he was in his natural, private, unpowdered state) by long chestnut hair. His eyebrows had a proudly perfect arch above clear deep-set eyes and, with his aquiline nose and finely modeled lips and chin, imparted to his countenance as a whole a far more "aristocratic" look than that which characterized the truly aristocratic count. Lavoisier's manners were as pleasing as his person. His essential seriousness had caused him to impose a spartan regimen on himself when most of his contemporaries, possessing his means, were involved in a succession of light love affairs and otherwise indulging themselves in the frivolities of Paris; but it did not follow from this that he was at all gauche in fashionable drawing rooms. He had, on the contrary, an abundance of savoir faire, thanks in part to his Aunt Constance's training and even more to the quiet deep self-confidence born of the love lavished on him as a child, his economic security, and the honors he had won at an unusually early age. Mlle. Marie Paulze was flattered by the attentions of so eminently eligible a bachelor. Very soon she deeply loved him.

His offer of marriage was accepted as soon as it was made; it was deemed well that Marie become a bride as quickly as possible, to forestall possible further aggressions by the Abbé Terray or the Comte d'Amerval. The marriage contract was signed on December 4, 1771. In it, Paulze agreed to pay 20,000 livres at once to the prospective groom and a balance of 60,000 during the next half-dozen years. If this seems a substantial amount, it was certainly not so large in the circumstances as to justify the charge sometimes made that Lavoisier married for money. He already had money; his annual profit from the *ferme* approximated the amount that Paulze was pledged to pay him over a period of six years. He also had, or soon would have, a patent of nobility, purchased for him by his father, Jean Antoine. The sale of such patents, whose owners became equerries to the king, was one of the ways that money was brought into the perpetually depleted royal treasury of Louis XV, and although Antoine Lavoisier seems never to have used the title thus conferred on him, he gained from it various privileges.

Far more important to Antoine's happiness than the size

of Marie's dowry was the fact that among the 200 guests who gathered at the home of Terray de Rozier, brother of the Abbé, to witness the signing of the contract, were the dowager Comtesse d'Amerval and the Abbé Terray himself. Paulze was saved from the ruin that had threatened him. The Abbé Terray, reconciled, offered his private chapel for the wedding ceremony, which was performed there just twelve days later, December 16, 1771. The couple then moved into a small mansion, in the Rue Neuve-des-Bons-Enfants, presented to them as a wedding gift by Antoine's father.

The husband was then twenty-eight. His bride was fourteen.

The child bride was destined never to become a mother, but she became much more than a typically loving wife and keeper of her husband's house. She knew her husband was a genius; she was determined to make herself the companion and collaborator of genius; and her natural abilities—her quick intelligence, her industry, and her self-discipline—were fully equal to the role. She put her talent for drawing at her husband's service, illustrating his scientific reports with accurate renditions of his experiments and equipment. She learned English to translate into French, for her husband's use, the current scientific papers of Englishmen, especially those of Joseph Priestley and of Henry Cavendish. She so trained herself in the techniques of science, under her husband's tutelage, that she was able to serve him as laboratory assistant; many of the entries in his now-classic laboratory notebooks are in her script.

First Steps Toward a New Chemistry

By the time Lavoisier was married, chemistry had clearly established itself as his principal scientific interest, outstripping such rivals for his attention as geology and meteorology. Actually, as exemplified by *The Analysis of Gypsum,* his interest in chemistry had grown directly out of his work with Guettard in mineralogy. When his method —employed in his mineralogical work—of determining the purity of water by use of sensitive hydrometers was criticized in 1767, he was stimulated to make his first truly important contribution to the transactions of the Academy.

What the hydrometer directly measures, of course, is the *density* of water—its weight per unit volume—but Lavoisier had assumed that this was tantamount to a measurement of purity since density increases with the quantity of dissolved impurities. In other words, the lower the density, the purer the water, the ultimate standard of purity is distilled water, whose density remains constant so long as its temperature is constant. The assumption—involving the constancy or unalterability of distilled (pure) water—was brought into question by the fact that when distilled water was evaporated to dryness in a glass vessel, a slight but palpable residue invariably was left. Le Roy, a chemist of distinguished reputation, explained this in a paper presented to the Academy, asserting that the addition to water of heat (then considered a "subtle" or "imponderable" fluid) resulted in the transmutation of water into earth.

To determine the truth or falsity of this assertion, Lavoisier, in the fall of 1768, devised an experiment similar to, if not modeled on, one conducted by the Englishman Joseph Black (1728-99) about thirteen years before.[6] Lavoisier bought from the official of the mint, named Chemin, who had made it, a balancing scale of such sensitivity that it would turn with the weight of a hair when carrying a load of five or six pounds. He also had a glassblower make a vessel whose peculiar shape had caused it in the days of the alchemists to be called a "pelican." When water poured into the base of a pelican was boiled, its vapor and steam went up the neck into an upper chamber, where because of the lower temperature, it condensed and then ran back down the neck into the base, where it was again vaporized. Thus, the same water could be distilled in the same vessel over and over.

Lavoisier's first step was to obtain water that had already been distilled eight times and was therefore, by his assumption, perfectly pure and unalterable. Using some of this

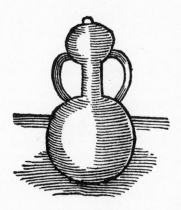

A pelican.

water, he carefully washed and dried the pelican; then he weighed it with extreme care, first in one pan of the balance and then in the other, recording the mean between the two readings as *the* weight. Next, he poured a measured quantity of water into the pelican and warmed it gently. As he did this, he removed the pelican's stopper from time to time so that some of the heated air might escape, reducing the danger of breakage by the pressure of expanding air. This done, he thrust the stopper hard into the pelican and weighed the vessel with its water in the same way that he had weighed it empty. Finally, he sealed the stopper in the pelican, which he placed in a sand bath * in such a way that whatever solid substance accumulated in the vessel's base would be observable. The preparations were now complete. On October 24, 1768, the actual experiment began.

Below the sand bath had been placed a lamp of six wicks, which were to be fed by a constant supply of olive oil and trimmed every twelfth hour. This lamp was now lighted, and it burned steadily, uninterruptedly for 101 days, maintaining a water temperature in the pelican of from 60 to 70 degrees on the Reaumur scale he used, or of from 167 to 192 degrees Fahrenheit. For the first 27 days of ceaseless distillation, nothing noticeable happened. Then Lavoisier saw some very fine particles dancing through the water, particles that appeared through a magnifying lens as irregularly shaped gray flakes. In the days immediately following, the flakes increased in size; but they ceased doing this after December 15, and after December 20 they settled to the vessel's bottom, the water above being again perfectly clear by the end of January, 1769.

On February 1, Lavoisier removed the heat from under the sand bath and removed the sealing stuff from the stopper, without removing the latter. He then weighed the pelican and found that it weighed precisely the same as it had when the experiment began. When the stopper was partly removed—a difficult operation, because of the partial vacuum inside the pelican—a hissing rush of outside air into the flask proved that no outside air had entered while the experiment was going on. This fact, combined with the equivalence of weight before and after, indicated conclusively to Lavoisier that neither air nor any other external substance had penetrated the glass of the pelican to produce the grayish flakes. Whence, then, came these flakes? Obviously they had come *either* from the transmuta-

* A sand bath is a container of heated sand used as an equable heater of retorts, etc., in chemical processes.

tion of water into earth which was hypothesized by the chemist Le Roy *or* from the pelican's glass walls. Chemin's delicately balanced scales would say which, and Lavoisier promptly appealed to them.

After emptying very carefully all the water and earth from the pelican and drying the latter, he weighed it and found that it had lost $17\frac{4}{10}$ grains of weight. He then dried the gray flakes, placed them in the scales, and found that they weighed $4\frac{9}{10}$ grains. There was a difference of $12\frac{5}{10}$ grains between the weight lost by the pelican and the weight of the flakes. What accounted for it? Probably this difference was the weight of glass material that remained still in solution, thought Lavoisier. This probability was increased when he tested the experimental water with his hydrometer and found it had a higher density than that of the distilled Seine water from which his experimental sample had been originally drawn. He therefore poured the water into a glass alembic and evaporated most of it, transferring what remained to a flat glass dish, wherein he carried the evaporation to dryness. Sure enough, there was a residue of gray flakes!

When he placed them on the scales, however, he found that they *more* than made up the weight difference for which he was trying to account: They weighed $15\frac{5}{10}$ grains, instead of $12\frac{5}{10}$, or precisely 3 grains more than they should have. Lavoisier realized almost at once that the increase of 3 grains, far from being a contradiction of his hypothetical explanation, was a further confirmation. He had poured the experimental water into a glass vessel, he had evaporated it in glass vessels, and according to his hypothesis, some of this glass material must dissolve into the water and remain as residue after evaporation was complete. Hence, the extra 3 grains.

This experiment, although it now seems to be of a child-ish simplicity, was of major importance to science if only because it developed the essential type of all of Lavoisier's later experimental work and, hence, of all laboratory chemistry. It was absolutely conclusive in its own terms. It proved what Lavoisier had initially assumed to be true—namely, that repeated distillations do not change the nature or properties of water, either by transmuting it into earth or by so "refining" it that it passes through the pores of glass (a theory then widely held) and that distilled water may therefore be used as a standard substance, provided the distillation process is carried out in containers that are not water-soluble. (That glass *is* slightly water-soluble was also proved.) But the experiment's greater, more fundamental importance lay, to repeat, in the *type* which it modeled—a type that insists on a rigorous and exclusive quantitativeness or, in other words, on the translation of all qualities into number readings on a quantitative scale. Whatever actually exists in the world as an object of scientific study *is* measurable in quantitative terms, and its accurate measurement is a *sine qua non* of the experimental method.

Although it was completed in February, 1769, and was described in a memoir received by the secretary of the Academy on May 10 of that year, Lavoisier's water experiment was not formally reported to the world until November 14, 1770. He read his memoir to a public meeting of the Academy on that date. The eighteen-month delay was caused by the secretary's wish to avoid undue public embarrassment of the distinguished Le Roy, whose memoir of 1767, now to a large degree discredited by Lavoisier's work, had been presented at a *rentrée publique* of the Academy (hence, Lavoisier's insistence that he be permitted to do the same) but was still unpublished in 1769. Indeed, the slowness of the publication of Academy transactions was a continuing source of frustration and irritation to scientists in those days; often two or three years intervened between the initialing of a memoir by the secretary and its appearance in print.

Meanwhile, Lavoisier was attacking the water problem on another front, that of sanitary and hydraulic engineering. An engineer, named De Parcieux, had made proposals for providing Paris with a sanitary water supply, and when he died in 1768, his proposals were taken up and strongly pressed by Lavoisier. "One is alarmed when one realizes that the inhabitants of this great capital are nourished on water carted from the Seine on the backs of men or beasts," he wrote in an article published in the *Mercure de France*. "The scarcity of water contributes enormously to uncleanliness of person and unhealthful air." When the proposals were publicly ridiculed, Lavoisier defended them so persuasively in a paper presented to the Academy that the city government adopted them; this action had no practical effect for a couple of decades, because of the chronic shortage of public money. The shortage also militated against the practical adoption of Lavoisier's proposal to establish a system of pumps whereby water would be available in sufficient amounts and at sufficient pressures to be used in the fighting of fires. In 1771 he presented to the Academy a paper in which he calculated, from barometric readings taken at various levels of the city and from other observations, the proper size and position of a steam pump for the Paris water supply.

He was also actively interested at this time in the problem of what happens to diamonds when they are heated—a problem that led him directly into a consideration of the problem of combustion in general, whose solution was to constitute his great, his revolutionary, achievement. For a century it had been repeatedly observed that diamonds were apparently destroyed when strongly heated, but it was not known whether the process was one of evaporation or combustion or crackling disintegration into particles. Lavoisier, in collaboration with two other investigators, proposed to find out, making precise use of his balancing scales, of course. The three men first established definitely that strongly heated in air, a diamond *did* lose weight and polish. They then proceeded to test the theory of a jeweler, named Maillard, who was convinced that the apparent evaporation of the diamond would not occur when it was heated in the absence of air. Using three diamonds furnished by Maillard for the purpose, Lavoisier and his colleagues demonstrated the truth of Maillard's hypothesis: Placed in a clay pipe that was first filled with powdered charcoal and then sealed, the diamonds were intensely heated for several hours without any loss of weight or polish. This work was reported to the Academy in a paper read on April 29, 1772.

The three men were now joined by a fourth person in an effort to determine precisely what happened when the diamond was heated in air. They obtained for this purpose the use of a great burning glass, the lens of Tschirnhausen, which had come to the Academy from the Duc d'Orléans and had been formerly used by scientists who were investigating the effect of heat on metals. This lens and another lens (also made by Baron Tschirnhausen) lent by a French nobleman were set up in August, 1772, in the Jardin de l'Infante, where full advantage could be taken of the noonday sun to produce at the lens' focus the highest temperatures which men could achieve at that time. The studies made then and continued in October of the following year proved that the diamond was combustible and had properties in common with many other combustibles—charcoal, whale oil, spirits of wine, and candles—because when it was heated in a confined—hence measurable—volume of ordinary air, it diminished the volume of the latter, while in the process of being itself "reduced" to "fixed air." Two tests showed the air above the "reduced" diamond to be "fixed"—to be the same, in other words, as the air with which Joseph Priestley was "impregnating" water that same year. One was the addition of limewater to it: A precipitate of powdered chalk was produced. The other was the introduction of a lighted candle to it: The flame was extinguished as promptly as if it had been snuffed between thumb and forefinger.

These conclusions about the combustion of diamonds derived not only from the diamond experiments of August, 1772, and October, 1773, but also from experiments with the combustion of phosphorus and sulfur conducted in September and October, 1772. From all these, Lavoisier conceived—vaguely, tentatively—a theory of the nature of combustion in general. Early in 1773 he initiated a long series of experiments deliberately designed to develop and test his theory, which, he predicted in a notebook entry for February 20 of that year, was "destined to bring about a revolution in physics and chemistry." What he learned from these studies affected the conclusions he finally drew from and about the diamond experiments.

Lavoisier could not complete his revolutionary theory, however, until a crucial piece of factual information, hitherto missing, was supplied by Joseph Priestley in the autumn of 1774 and the spring of 1775.

3. Priestley the Experimenter

Fire and Air: The Quantitative Approach of English Chemists

To appreciate Joseph Priestley's remarkable experimental work in his laboratory at Bowood, some knowledge of the development of chemistry to that time is required. As the Introduction to this book records, mechanistic theory had scored a seemingly absolute triumph in virtually every field of knowledge as the eighteenth century opened. Kepler, Galileo, and Newton had shown the universe to be a vast machine, every part of which—the largest, as well as the smallest—operated according to mechanical laws. It followed that the terms of mechanism were the only ones in which any problem could be truly stated and solved, whether that problem was of man and his society or of the natural world around him. Such was the deep-seated belief, the all-pervasive assumption, in leading minds.

But this triumph of mechanism was absolute, or seemingly so, *only* in the realm of general theory. In the realm of particular practice the terms of mechanism were very un-evenly applied among the various fields of knowledge, or classes of problems. They were rigorously and universally applied to the problems of physics and astronomy, the fields in which the terms had been originally defined; they were very loosely and partially applied to the problems of medicine and chemistry (chemistry was then largely the handmaiden of medicine), with the result that these fields remained weird mixtures of precise knowledge, vague spec-ulation, and magical nonsense. Whereas astronomy had freed itself from astrology and theology, and physics from theology and metaphysics, eighteenth-century chemistry was very imperfectly divorced from medieval alchemy and the cosmology of the Greek philosophers. The picturesque but hopelessly unsystematic nomenclature of alchemy con-tinued to be employed—chemical substances still went by such names as "oil of vitriol," "powder of Algaroth," "salt of alembroth," "flowers of zinc," and "butter of antimony" —and chemical theory still embraced, in various ways and to varying degrees, the four "elements" of Empedocles (*circa* 440 B.C.); namely, fire, earth, air, and water. There were few unambiguous definitions of the things and proc-esses which chemistry purported to explain or describe. Chaos reigned over the field.

But not altogether: There was a segment where order prevailed as the Age of Reason opened, and for this the pioneering work of Robert Boyle was largely responsible. Boyle, the seventh son of the Earl of Cork, was one of the founders of the Royal Society, and it is significant that he came to chemistry by way of physics, scoring his suc-cesses in the former field by applying to it the mechanistic principles defined in the latter. Boyle made several addi-tions to the body of specific chemical knowledge. He dis-covered methyl alcohol, and he prepared copper chloride by applying mercuric chloride to copper (to use modern nomenclature rather than that available to Boyle). He also observed that iron filings treated with a mineral acid yielded a highly flammable "air"—the earliest recorded observation of hydrogen. But by far his greatest contribution to chemical science was in essence a philosophical one in the tradition of Francis Bacon, who profoundly influenced him.

In *The Sceptical Chymist* (published first in 1661) Boyle heaped ridicule on the ambiguities, inconsistencies, and pretensions of the chemists of his day while issuing a clarion call for precise definitions and close reasoning. He complained of the "unreasonable liberty" chemists gave themselves "of playing with names at pleasure." He scorned their incapacity for plain, unequivocal statements. He more than suspected that they wrote "thus darkly, not because they think their notions too precious to be explained, but because they fear that if they were explained, men would discern that they are far from being precious." Of course, "they cannot write otherwise than confusedly of what they but confusedly apprehend," but he hoped that "judicious men skilled in chymical affairs" would "agree to write clearly and plainly of them, and thereby keep men from being stunned . . . or imposed upon by dark and empty words." Those who could not write in this way might then be discouraged from writing at all and so cease "to trouble the world with riddles and impertinencies."

Boyle was especially critical of the failure of chemists to define clearly the key term "element"—a failure which rendered meaningless the conceptions of "mixtures" and "compounds." His own definition laid a cornerstone of chemical science and also anticipated, if it did not actually help shape, the distinction between "primary" and "secondary" qualities made in John Locke's *Essay Concerning Human Understanding* (published in 1690). Boyle held the world to be made of one "Catholick or Universal Matter," which was divided into infinitesimal fragments—atoms, corpuscles—having size and shape and local motion. These were *minima* or *prima naturalia* in his Latin terminology, and they came together in primary clusters, which were the smallest units into which a perfectly homogeneous chemical substance could be broken down. Variations in the microscopic local motions of these primary clusters determined the seemingly infinite diversity of objects, each of which possessed in itself definite size and shape and other primary qualities that impressed on perceiving minds such effects—secondary qualities—as color, temperature, and odor. The primary clusters varied in kind, and each kind constituted what Boyle called an "element."

"I must advertise to you," he wrote, "that I now mean by Elements . . . certain primitive and simple, or perfectly unmingled bodies which not being made of any other bodies . . . are the ingredients of which all those called perfectly mixed bodies are immediately compounded, and into which they are ultimately resolved." Or to put it another way: "I must not look upon any body as a true principle or element, but as yet compounded, which is not perfectly homogeneous, but is further resoluble into any number of distinct substances, how small soever."

While yet in his early twenties, in collaboration with Robert Hooke (1635-1703), whom he had hired to build an improved air pump, Boyle conducted a series of fundamental experiments on what he called "the spring [meaning the elasticity] of air." They were experiments whose implicit assumption was Newton's third law, which asserts that for every action there is an equal and opposite reaction. In the cylinder of the pump, which Boyle termed his "pneumatical engine," a precisely measurable pressure could be exerted by the piston on a precisely measurable volume of air, enabling Boyle to discern an inversely proportionate relationship between the two measurements.

When he doubled the pressure, the volume was halved. His general conclusion, still known as Boyle's law, is expressed in one of the basic equations of physics:

$$\frac{V_1}{V} \;=\; \frac{P}{P_1}$$

P refers to the smaller pressure and V to the volume of an ideal gas under this pressure, and P_1 refers to the greater pressure and V_1 to the volume of ideal gas under this pressure. Thus was prepared the way for experiments in pneumatic chemistry wherein an investigator might partially infer the nature of a chemical reaction from its effect in increasing or decreasing an initially given volume of air (gas) kept at a constant temperature and pressure.

Boyle and Hooke also determined that when a bell is rung inside a jar from which the air has been evacuated, no sound issues; that insects and animals cannot live—nor can a candle burn—in the absence of air; and that gunpowder burns as well in a vacuum as in air. The last two observations led them to conclude that "something" in the air which is necessary to combustion and the respiration of animals—phenomena evidently related in kind to each other—is also present in saltpeter or niter, which is the essential ingredient of gunpowder. (Saltpeter is potassium nitrate, KNO_3.) Hence, ordinary air was not an element, as defined by Boyle; it was not a perfectly homogeneous substance but, instead, a mixture. Hooke said so explicitly in early 1667, asserting that "*the dissolution* of sulphurous bodies is made by a substance inherent, and mixt with the Air, that is like, if not the very same, with that which is fixt in *Salt-Peter*." In other words, what the saltpeter gave up when it burned was precisely what the "sulphurous bodies" took up when *they* burned.

The connection between respiration and combustion was still more closely made during the next two years by

John Mayow (1643-79), a physician in Bath who was led by the Boyle-Hooke experiments to make investigations of his own along the same lines. (Mayow became a Fellow of the Royal Society in the year before his early death.) It had been known by the natural philosophers of ancient Alexandria that when a candle is burned inside a glass vessel inverted over water, the water level rises steadily in the vessel until the candle goes out, the level remaining constant thereafter. Mayow substituted a live mouse for a candle and found that essentially the same thing happened: The water level rose until the mouse died, then remained stationary. He also discovered that when a mouse and a lighted candle were placed together in a closed container of air, the candle went out first, and then the mouse died; but that a mouse lived twice as long in the container if no lighted candle was placed beside it there.

Mayow then devised an experiment to test Hooke's conclusion that the "substance" enabling gunpowder to burn in a vacuum was the same as that which, "mixt with the Air," enabled "sulphurous bodies" to burn. In enclosed air in which a candle had been burnt to extinction or a mouse had breathed until it died of suffocation, he burnt gunpowder and found that the foul enclosed air was restored: A candle would again burn in it; a mouse could again breathe in it. He inferred that air is indeed a mixture of two kinds of particle, only one of which is active in the support of fire and of breathing. He called this kind nitro-aerial because such particles were present both in niter and in "good" air.

The next step toward a recognition of the nature of combustion was taken by Boyle. In a pamphlet describing his "new experiments," issued in 1673, he told how he had weighed a piece of tin, heated it until it became what was then called a calx (an oxide), and, then as a last step, weighed the calx. He found the latter was heavier than the original tin. From the fact that the weight increase resulted from the application of heat, he inferred that heat must be a "ponderable matter" that had united with the tin to form the calx. The experiment showed, said he, "that it is possible to render the parts of fire stable and ponderable"—a grossly erroneous conclusion, which had, nevertheless, the great merit of emphasizing the importance of weight measurements in chemical experiment and of describing combustion as a process of combination or addition, rather than of reduction or subtraction.* It had also the merit, inadvertent on Boyle's part, of stimulating experiments along the same line by Mayow, who concluded that the weight increase that occurred when he heated tin with a burning lens was due to the addition to the tin, not of "heat" or "parts of fire," but of the nitro-aerial particles whose existence he had inferred from his earlier observations.

Further study of what we now call "gases" (a term first used by Jan Baptista van Helmont [1577?-1644], who derived it from the Greek word for "chaos") and of what Englishmen in Priestley's time continued to call "airs" was inhibited in the late seventeenth century by the fact that no adequate method of collecting and storing them had been devised. Mayow, it is true, employed a primitive species of pneumatic trough, but the practical invention of this important piece of chemical laboratory equipment was not made until 1726, when Stephen Hales (1677-1761) first

---

* Boyle was by no means the first person to observe the weight increase of a metal upon calcination. A French doctor of medicine, Jean Rey (his exact dates are unknown, but he lived in the early seventeenth century), published in 1630 *The Increase in Weight of Tin and Lead on Calcination*. In startling anticipation of Lavoisier's work a century and a half later, Rey concluded: "That this increase in weight comes from the air, which in the vessel has been rendered denser, heavier, and in some measure adhesive, by the vehement and long-continued heat of the furnace: which air mixes with the calx (frequent agitation aiding) and becomes attracted to its most minute particles...." [1]

used it to collect and store an "inflammable air" produced by the burning of Newcastle coal.

Hales, a clergyman who became a Fellow of the Royal Society in 1717 and a winner of its Copley Medal in 1739, has been called the "father of vegetable physiology." He conducted fundamental researches into the ways in which plants use water, accomplishing the difficult feat of measur-

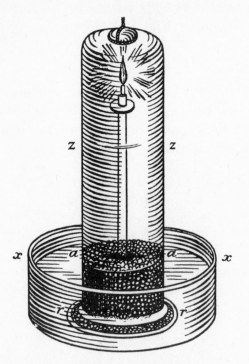

Hales' experiments on combustion and respiration. The inverted glass *zzaa*, suspended by a cord, had its mouth some inches under the surface of the water. A siphon was used to draw air out of the glass until the water reached the level *aa*. The water rose to *zz* when combustion or breathing destroyed a part of the air's elasticity, the quantity being indicated by the resultant space *aazz*. If an air-generating matter was placed on the pedestal where the candle is above, the water to begin with was established at level *zz* and then subsided to *aa*, the difference in heights showing the quantity of air generated.

ing their rates of imbibition and respiration, and he was led by these researches to inquire specifically into the nature of "air." As he put it in his *Vegetable Staticks* (published in 1727): "Having produced many Experiments, to prove that the Air is plentifully inspired by Vegetables, not only at their roots, but also thro' several parts of their trunks and branches ... this put me upon making a more particular inquiry into the nature of a Fluid which is so absolutely necessary for the support of the life and growth of Animals and Vegetables." Using quantitative methods, he studied the respiration of animals, repeating with improving modifications "Dr. Mayow's Experiment, to find out how much air is absorbed by the breath of Animals inclosed in glasses" and to compare this absorption with that of a burning candle. He also made "an Attempt to analyse the Air, by a great variety of Chymio-Statical Experiments," to quote the descriptive subtitle he gave *Vegetable Staticks*. He produced gaseous ammonia by heating sal ammoniac with lime, he attributed to the "addition" of some substance the weight increase of lead calcined into red lead, and he described combustion as the "action and reaction of the aerial and sulphurous particles." He did not, however, recognize the existence of different kinds of "air." He continued to regard atmospheric air as a single substance, a true element whose different properties—as in gaseous ammonia, coal gas, and the expired breath of animals—were due wholly to "impurities."

Hales' improved pneumatic trough, pictured above in an original illustration from *Vegetable Staticks,* greatly facilitated his studies of "the Air" in general. But his use of water in the trough prevented his noticing any gas (or "property" of "impure" air, as he might initially have said) which was water-soluble. Had he used mercury, instead of water in his trough, as Priestley was to do, he might have gained the distinction of discovering "fixed air." Indeed, Mayow before him might have done so had Mayow inverted his glass vessel enclosing a burning candle over mercury, instead of over water. The "fixed air" produced by the candle is insoluble in mercury but highly soluble in water, as we saw in the case of Priestley's "soda

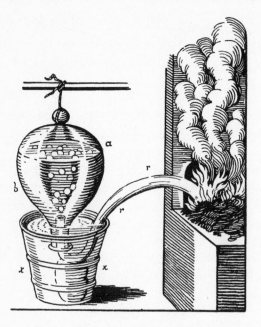

Hales' improved pneumatic trough.

water." Hence, there would have been no rise in the level of the liquid mercury within the enclosing vessel as the candle burned to extinction, the gaseous pressure on the liquid surface inside remaining the same as the atmospheric pressure on the liquid surface outside. The discrepancy between "air" pressure over water and "air" pressure over mercury, in these circumstances, could hardly have failed to stimulate so acute an observer as Mayow, and so ingenious an experimenter, to inquire successfully into the reason for it.

But all this lies in the realm of unrealized possibility. In the actual event, the distinction of proving that the earth's atmosphere is a mixture, rather than a single element, was gained by Joseph Black (1728-99), whose crucial experiments, which are generally believed to have become the model for Lavoisier's, entitle him to be called the founder of quantitative pneumatic chemistry.

Black was born of Scottish parents in Bordeaux, France, where his father was at the time engaged in the wine trade. He went to school in Belfast, Ireland, and he studied medicine and chemistry at the University of Glasgow and the University of Edinburgh, in Scotland, in both of which he later taught these subjects. It was a specific medical problem that led him into his most important chemical research. When, in 1753 or 1754, he began his experiments with quicklime, *magnesia alba* (magnesium carbonate, $MgCO_3$), and other alkaline substances, he was in search of a more powerful agent than was then available for the dissolution of the stones that sometimes form in the human urinary bladder. This initial and specific interest did not, however, blind him to the significance of the remarkable weight equivalents he soon discovered through his unprecedentedly precise use of the balance at every stage of his investigation.

It had long been known that when limestone is strongly heated (calcined), it is transformed into quicklime, or *produces* quicklime, which is caustic—that is, capable of burning human flesh. It had also long been known that, in general, mild alkalies can be rendered caustic through treatment with limewater. Although *magnesia alba* was regarded by Black as a mild alkali and perhaps even as a species of limestone at the outset of his experiments, he found that a treatment of it with limewater produced no caustic solution. He then tried to make a carefully weighed sample caustic by heating it strongly. He was astonished to find that it lost a full seven-twelfths of its weight through such heating. When he tested the five-twelfths of residue, he found that it dissolved in the same common acids as did the original *magnesia alba* and produced, in interaction with such acids, the same salts (compounds of acids and metal, as we now know). But this residue did *not* effervesce in the process of dissolution—as did the original *magnesia alba*—nor did it precipitate limewater.

His next effort was to explain experimentally the missing weight. Something had been lost. What was it? He heated a precisely weighed sample of *magnesia alba* in a retort from which he could collect the issuing vapors. The vapors condensed into liquid water, which, he found, accounted for but a small part of the total weight loss. The difference, he concluded, must be the weight of an uncondensable "air," whose loss was also indicated by the fact that the original sample effervesced as it dissolved, whereas the heated residue did not. He then calcined another precisely weighed sample of *magnesia alba;* weighed the calx, recording the precise weight loss; dissolved this calx in "oil of vitriol" (sulfuric acid, H_2SO_4); and reprecipitated it as a solid powder by adding alkali to the acid solution. Carefully collecting the precipitate, he weighed it and found it precisely the same weight as the original sample (precisely, that is, within the smallest possible margin of experimental error) and to have the same general properties: It effervesced in acids, and it precipitated limewater. Evidently it *was* again ordinary *magnesia alba*. Black concluded that the "air" which had been lost through heating was restored by the precipitating alkali—a confirmation of Hales' observation that alkaline salts when acted on by acids give up an "air" that is "fixed" in them.

Further confirming experiments were then devised by

Black. He took a precisely weighed quantity of pure fixed alkaline salt (sodium carbonate, Na_2CO_3) and mixed it to saturation with a precisely weighed quantity of diluted oil of vitriol. He found the mixture weighed *less* than the combined weights of the original ingredients. Approximately the same thing happened when he saturated oil of vitriol with magnesia: This mixture, too, lost weight. But when he calcined precisely the same amount of magnesia, weighed the calx, and dissolved it in diluted oil of vitriol, he found that the weight of the solution equaled the combined weights of calx and acid. There was *no* weight loss. Moreover, approximately the same amount of acid was required to dissolve the calx of an ounce of magnesia as that required to dissolve the original ounce. Thus, all experimental evidence confirmed Black's conclusion that the difference between uncalcined and calcined magnesia was due to the "considerable quantity of air" present in the former and absent from the latter. It was due to what he called "fixed air," borrowing the term first used by Hales.

Nor did Black stop there. He experimented with chalk and found that heating it to make quicklime resulted in the same kind of weight loss owing to the release of the same kind of "fixed air" as that which resulted from the calcination of magnesia. He found, too, that when acid was poured over chalk, "fixed air" bubbled through the solvent and could be collected in a container inverted over it. He was enabled to make some study (although ill health prevented his making a detailed one) of the nature and properties of this gas, which is now known as carbon dioxide (CO_2). He found that it would not support combustion (nothing would burn in its presence alone); that it occurred as a small constituent of atmospheric air and could be removed by bubbling air through limewater, forming a chalky precipitate in such water; that it was a product of the fermentation of beer; that it was a product of the combustion of charcoal; and that it was expired from the lungs as a man breathed.

The specific knowledge thus gained was of major importance in the history of science. So was the invention of the method by which future discoveries of the same sort might be made. Of at least equal historical importance was the fact that Black's work struck the first heavy blow against a false theory of burning that dominated chemical thinking in his time—a theory he himself accepted (insofar as he accepted any general theory) and continued to hold even after his blow against it had been delivered.

The Phlogiston Theory: The Speculative Approach of Continental Chemists

This theory was initially the work of a German, Johann Joachim Becher (1635-82), who lived as a contemporary of Boyle, Hooke, and Mayow (he was born in the same year as Hooke) but who was not in any close correspondence with them and whose approach to chemical problems was very different from theirs. Hooke's pregnant experimental inference in 1667 showed that saltpeter has in common with atmospheric air a "substance" necessary for *"the dissolution* of sulphurous bodies." Mayow's immediately following work showed not only that an animal's breathing and a candle's burning are chemically similar processes, but also that "bad" air can be made "good" through the burning of saltpeter in it. An interesting historical coincidence is the fact that Mayow was conducting the latter experiments, which pointed clearly in the right direction, in the very year (1669) that Becher published his *Physica Subterranea,* which pointed, if far less clearly, in the *wrong* direction.

Becher had no such penchant for exact quantitative observation, using rigorously objective measurements, as that which Boyle and Boyle's followers manifested in England. His was a speculative, rather than an experimental, mind. Moreover, as a scientific theorist, he possessed grave weaknesses: He was addicted to the classifying habit of mind (like Aristotle's), deducing consequences from classifying statements, and he failed to practice the consistency of basic definition which Boyle called for in *The Sceptical Chymist*. Nevertheless, some historians of science assert that he deserves honor for suggesting the first "rational" theory of combustion and that the general effect of his theory, at least at first, was more helpful than harmful to the progress of chemistry.

Becher's theory, briefly stated, was as follows:

Combustion is a process of decomposition; it is the dissolution of the combustible body into its constituents. From this it follows that no simple body, consisting of a single substance, is combustible, for it has no parts into which it can be decomposed. But not every composite body is combustible. Combustion is a specific effect, and every such effect must have a specific cause. Hence, every combustible body possesses, as the cause of its combustibility, a "something" which Becher called *terra pinguis* or "oily earth" ("fatty earth"). This is expelled from the body during combustion, and only "stony" or "vitreous" earth is left behind. Some combustibles contain more *terra pinguis* than others, a fact "explaining" their greater combustibility. The mineral substances that are combustible contain, in general, very little. Charcoal, on the other hand, is almost pure *terra pinguis;* thus, it leaves only a very slight amount of ash when it burns.

But it was not as Becher left it that the theory achieved its enormous fame and influence. For the latter development the credit belongs to Becher's pupil and follower, Georg Ernst Stahl (1660-1734). It was Stahl who substituted for the term *terra pinguis* the word "phlogiston," which (ironically) he borrowed from Boyle's masterpiece of 1661, the book in which Boyle inveighed against chemists' "playing with names," and it is with Stahl's name that the phlogiston doctrine is primarily associated in history. The theory "formed the groundwork of chemical research for the next fifty years," wrote James Campbell Brown in his *History of Chemistry*, "dominated the minds of philosophers for a hundred years, and was the outstanding fact of chemical history in the eighteenth century." [2] When Priestley was first introduced to chemistry, "the doctrine of Stahl" was universally considered, as he later wrote, to be "the greatest discovery that had been made in the science." Priestley himself had a reverential regard for it in the 1770's, as he conducted his experiments at Bowood. So did nearly all other chemists. Lavoisier, depositing a sealed note with the secretary of the Academy of Science on November 1, 1772, said that he did so to protect his right to a "discovery appearing to me one of the most interesting of those that have been made since the time of Stahl," indicating his view that Stahl's, up to that time, was the greatest name in chemistry. That this should be so appears to present-day eyes one of the curiosities of intellectual history, for Stahl's own statements of his doctrine are so ambiguous in their meaning—so hopelessly confused in respect to "matter," "essence," and "principle," none of which is clearly defined—as to render them essentially unintelligible.

His clearest statements are to the effect that *phlogiston is the principle of combustibility*. But this, standing alone, is an unmitigated tautology: "combustibility" is the "combustibility" of "combustibility." In other statements the "principle" becomes "material"—an actual ingredient of combustible bodies, as Becher had held "oily" earth to be. "It is to be kept in mind," Stahl wrote, "that as well in the fat with which one smears his shoes, as in the sulphur of the mines and all metals [that are] partly or wholly combustible, there is actually the same essence (or principle) which gives and constitutes its inflammability." His most widely quoted passage is almost incomprehensible: "Briefly, in the act of composition, as an instrument, there intervenes and is most potent, fire, flaming, fervent, hot; but [in] the very substance of the compound there intervenes, as an ingredient, as it is commonly called, as a material principle and as a constituent part of the whole compound, the *material and principle of fire,* not fire itself. This I was the first to call Phlogiston." [3]

Stahl "explained" the fact that a lamp will not burn in a closed vessel by asserting, on the basis of no experimental evidence at all, that phlogiston assumed a rapid whirling motion, requiring much open space, as it was expelled from the burning body. Where there was insufficient room for this motion, the phlogiston could not leave the combustible body—that is to say, the body could not burn. A more sophisticated "explanation" was developed in the later phlogiston theory; namely, the air has a limited capacity to absorb the fire principle and, when saturated, acts as a barrier to the escape of phlogiston. Fire will not burn in a thoroughly phlogisticated air because there is no place where more phlogiston can go.

As for metals and their calxes, the phlogiston theory held the latter to be simpler in composition than the former. Iron, tin, and lead were deemed to be compounds of metal plus phlogiston. Their calxes were what was left after the phlogiston had been expelled through combustion. It must be confessed that a certain plausibility is attached to the explanation thus made of the most familiar of the industrial chemical processes in Stahl's time; namely, the smelting of metallic ores to obtain the usable metal.

Consider, for instance, the smelting of iron ore (iron oxide). According to the phlogiston theory, the ore is a substance lacking phlogiston. It is incombustible. But when this ore is mixed with charcoal and strongly heated, it becomes combustible. Why? Because the ore absorbs phlogiston from the charcoal with which it is in contact, charcoal being almost pure phlogiston. The reaction is as follows:

$$\text{Iron ore} + \text{phlogiston} \longrightarrow \text{metallic iron}$$

The theory seemed also to explain what happens when lime is burnt and when mild alkalies are made caustic through contact with slaked lime. In both cases, said the theory, there is a transfer of phlogiston: The burnt lime becomes caustic when phlogiston from the fire pours into it; potash and soda become caustic when phlogiston from the slake lime pours into them, leaving mild lime behind. The latter reaction is as follows:

$$\text{Mild alkali} + (\text{mild lime} + \text{phlogiston}) \longrightarrow$$
$$(\text{mild alkali} + \text{phlogiston}) + \text{mild lime}$$

Joseph Black's experiments cannot be said actually to have disproved the phlogiston hypothesis as it applied to magnesia, lime, potash, and soda. Phlogiston might indeed play the part it was alleged to play in the above reaction. But there was no evidence that it did so or even that it existed. If it did, the scales gave no sign of it. It must indeed be as weightless as an idea—a superfluous idea at that, since the facts could be fully explained without it. There was so perfect a correlation between (a) the presence or absence of fixed air in precisely measurable amounts and (b) the changes in causticity and in the capacity to effervesce in acids as to imply a causal connection between (a) and (b). The causticity of lime was evidently caused by the loss of fixed air. The restoration of mildness to lime was evidently caused by the gain of fixed air. There was no need to assume that phlogiston entered at all into the transaction.

But Black's resort to the balance for clues to the nature of chemical reactions and his use of it as a final arbiter of laboratory truth or error were not widely imitated in England, and still less so on the Continent, during the two decades immediately following his great experiments. The phlogiston theory continued to be accepted as true by virtually all chemists, who deemed it as fundamental to their science as Newton's laws of mechanics were to physics. The embarrassing fact that metallic calxes weigh more than the original metal was largely ignored, along with the fact that no calx is formed of metals heated in a vacuum. Even when the weight-change problem had at last to be faced squarely the theory found resourceful defenders. They sought to remove the difficulty by endowing the formerly weightless fire principle with the very *opposite* of weight. Ancient Greek philosophers, from the observation that flames always rise, had concluded that fire has the property of levity (lightness). Phlogistonists of the 1770's and 1780's, some of them, reached the same conclusion.[4] Phlogiston, they asserted, did indeed possess levity, the opposite of gravity. It had *negative* weight. Hence, when phlogiston was added to a substance, as in the smelting of iron, the substance lost weight. When phlogiston was removed from a substance, as in the formation of iron calx, the substance gained weight.

Such speculative ingenuity foundered on the fact that a negative weight should be as definitely measurable in a balance as a positive one, and no measure of it appeared in quantitative experiment. Indeed, in the light of such an experiment, a phlogiston endowed with levity was quickly seen to be less satisfactory by far than a phlogiston possessing no weight at all. Every weight change in Black's experiments, for instance, was fully accounted for by the gain or loss of fixed air. The data left no single gap into which a "negative mass" of phlogiston might be inserted.

The "Experimentarian Philosopher" *

Joseph Priestley was a convinced phlogistonist in 1773, when he went to work in the laboratory he established in a room at one end of the long library at Bowood. This is not remarkable: There was at the time no alternative general theory against which the phlogiston doctrine might be measured. But it *is* remarkable that Priestley remained a phlogistonist—and an ardent one—even after his greatest discovery had led directly to the development of a new general theory, one that gained almost universal acceptance before he died. Among the last of his scientific publications was a pamphlet, entitled *Considerations on the Doctrine of Phlogiston, and on the Decomposition of Water,* which was issued in Philadelphia, Pennsylvania, in 1796. In it he warmly defended the "doctrine of Stahl" against "what is now usually termed *the new system of chemistry,* or that of the *Antiphlogistians.*" The fact that "we are not able to ascertain the *weight* of phlogiston" was, he admitted, a "difficulty" of the old theory. "But neither do any of us pretend to have weighed *light,* or the element of *heat,* though we do not doubt that they are properly *substances* capable by their addition, or abstraction, of making great changes in the properties of bodies, and of being transmitted from one substance to another." [5]

All this adds up to one of the famous ironies in the history of science. It is also a psychological significant irony. This is the reason that it is mentioned here before

* The quotation is from Thomas Hobbes (1588-1679), the English philosopher whose masterpiece is his *Leviathan* and who regarded Priestley's kind of "natural philosophy" with contempt.

the work from which the irony springs has been described. For it should be emphasized that as a man of science, Priestley was "timorous" and "conservative"—in the words of T. E. Thorpe [6]—only in the realm of general theory. In the realm of particular facts he was bold and often marvelously ingenious. Moreover, it is an open question whether he could have contributed to science as richly as he was now about to do, had his been a theoretical system-building mind. The possessors of such minds often incline toward a kind of intellectual arrogance joined to an excessively inhibiting self-criticism—a self-criticism rooted, actually, in the arrogance it serves to check since its essence is a fear of being caught in humiliating error. Such men often lack the humility of mind—the humble willingness to submit their minds wholly to external fact—which is necessary for swiftly accurate observations of the natural world.

There are, after all, two general ways of science—one empirical (*i.e.,* experimental in a hit-or-miss fashion), the other systematic. Both are necessary in the development of scientific knowledge, neither is wholly exclusive of the other at any stage of the development, but the importance of the empirical, compared with the systematic, is greatly diminished as a science progresses from youth to maturity. "In the historical order of the development of a science," writes Arthur Pap, "the first step usually consists in the experimental verification of various logically independent laws; this body of laws is thereafter systematized by a comprehensive theory." [7] To put it another way, experience is a precondition of wisdom, in a developing science as in a growing man. A general law, whereby future observations may be predicted, cannot be shaped until a multitude of past observations is recorded.

Now Priestley, operating as a pioneer in pneumatic chemistry, was the empirical researcher par excellence. As has been said, his function was to accumulate through more or less random observations—carefully made, precisely reported—the raw materials, the "brute facts," out of which genuine scientific knowledge might be manufactured. His success in this enterprise required an ability to recognize the *significant* fact, and this in turn required his possession of at least rudimentary theories or hypotheses which might measure relative significance. His grasp of these, however, was slight: It is a paradoxical but probably true statement that he would have abandoned the phlogiston doctrine very soon, as a result of his own discoveries, had he grasped this theory and its implications more firmly, more completely. Theories in themselves— scientific theories—simply did not interest him very much, and he made small use of them as determinants of the direction or form of his researches. Instead, he depended very largely on fortunate contingencies (so-called "happy accidents") for his successes. In this he was like the solitary old-time prospector of the American West, who was trained to recognize precious ore when he saw it and who possessed some slight knowledge of the kind of rock formation in which ore of this sort was most likely to occur, but whose main reliance was on lucky chances as he roamed the wilderness.

We have seen how the accident of Priestley's having moved into a house in Leeds next door to a brewery, where an abundance of "fixed air" was available above the fermentation vats, led him into his first experiments in pneumatic chemistry. These suggested further experiments, not in terms of an underlying theory or overall hypothesis, but directly, on a strictly *ad hoc* basic. One thing led to another until there had been formed "a web of experiments uninterrupted by reasoning," as Lavoisier later called it with some justification, if with less than full justice. It was a web that caught and held a mass of useful, if unrelated, facts—more items of specific information than would have been gained in all likelihood by any man who insisted on organizing his external observations into an internally consistent body of knowledge.

Some of Priestley's apparatus, illustrated in his *Experiments and Observations on Different Kinds of Air.*

Priestley was willing to try anything in his laboratory, even things that appeared in the light of "reasoning" and earlier experiment to be certain of failure. For instance, by 1771 it had been established through experiment and observation that air is as necessary to vegetable as to animal life. From this it was "reasonable" to conclude that vegetable respiration and animal respiration would "use up" common air in the same way, rendering air unfit to support a candle's flame or a mouse's breathing. "I own I had that expectation when I first put a sprig of mint into a glass jar standing inverted over a vessel of water," reported Priestley, "but when it had continued there for some months I found the air would neither extinguish the candle, nor was it at all inconvenient to a mouse, which I put into it. . . ." This suggested that there was "something attending vegetation which restored air that had been injured by respiration" and that "the same process might also restore the air that had been injured by the burning of candles."

He went on: "Accordingly, on the 17th of August 1771, I put a sprig of mint into a quantity of air in which a wax candle had burned out, and found that on the 27th of the same month another candle burned perfectly well in it. This experiment I repeated, without the least variation in the event, not less than eight or ten times in the remainder of the summer."

He then proceeded to test whether "this remarkable effect" depended on something "peculiar to *mint*, which was the plant I always made use of till July 1772." On July 16 "I found a quantity of this kind of air to be perfectly restored by sprigs of *balm*, which had grown in it from the 7th of the same month." The same thing happened when he tried other plants, although "the most effectual of any kind that I have tried for this purpose is *spinach*, which is of quick growth but will seldom thrive long in water." His final step was a series of experiments to determine whether plant respiration was as effective in restoring air "Infected with Animal Respiration or Putrefaction" as it was in restoring "Air in which a Candle has burned out." He found that it was, and he concluded that this was one of the methods whereby "Nature" prevented "the whole mass of the atmosphere" from becoming "in time . . . unfit for the purpose of animal life." He cited a number of decisive experiments he conducted to prove "that plants, instead of affecting the air in the same manner with animal respiration, reverse the effects of breathing and tend to keep the atmosphere sweet and wholesome when it is become noxious in consequence of animals either living and breathing, or dying and putrefying in it." [8] (What he was here the first man to notice scientifically was, of course, an effect of the process now called "photosynthesis." In the presence of light the chlorophyll or green stuff in the leaves of plants uses the carbon of carbon dioxide, which it takes from the air, to make carbohydrates. Free oxygen is thereby released to the atmosphere.)

Simultaneously with these experiments, Priestley conducted others that were related to them, in his mind, only by the fact that they too dealt with air. Some of these other experiments were suggested by Hales' essays. Hales had observed that when air was confined above a paste formed of sulfur, iron filings, and water, its volume was notably reduced; evidently the paste absorbed some of the air. Priestley, repeating this experiment, found that about a fifth of the air's volume was thus absorbed and that the residual air was lighter than common air, would not support animal life, and produced no reaction with limewater (this meant that it was *not* "fixed air"). We now know that this residual "air" was almost wholly nitrogen, which makes up approximately four-fifths of the earth's atmosphere, and it is possible that Priestley, as a result of this and subsequent experiments, would have recognized it as a distinct and separate "air" had his mental vision not been blinkered by the phlogiston theory. The theory told him, however, that this residual air was as it was because it had become filled with phlogiston; it had become "phlogisticated" from the metal filings, which were calcined.

Hales had also treated iron pyrites with "spirit of niter"

(nitric acid, HNO_3) and found that there was generated an "air" which, mingled with common air, formed a thick red cloud. It appeared to Hales that there was "an equal diminution" in the volumes of the two airs as they interacted over water in his pneumatic trough. Priestley, who said that he was "particularly struck" by the phenomenon Hales reported, was eager to repeat the experiment but had at hand no pyrites. He finally proceeded on the assumption, suggested by a fellow scientist, that the peculiar "air" derived from the "spirit of niter," rather than from the pyrites. The assumption proved correct. He applied the "spirit" to several different metals—iron, copper, and silver —and found that in each case there was produced the peculiar new "air." That it *was* new and distinctive he proved through a series of experiments designed to test its properties. He named it "nitrous air," confessing that although he did not "altogether like the term," neither he nor his friends had "been able to hit upon a better." We now call it nitric oxide (NO).

He observed more precisely than Hales had been able to do the reduction in volume that occurred when "nitrous air" was mixed with common air over water to produce the red fumes. He found that the "diminution" amounted to "about a fifth of the common air, and as much of the nitrous air as is necessary to produce that effect; which, as I have found by many trials, is about one half as much as the original quantity of common air." In other words, he found that the maximum reduction occurred when he mixed 1 volume of the new "air" with 2 volumes of the "best" available atmospheric air. The reduction in this case was astonishingly large. Within a few minutes the original 3 volumes—1 of "nitrous" air and 2 of the "best" common air—were reduced to approximately 1.8 volumes, or 10 percent *less* than the volume of the atmospheric air alone before the "nitrous air" was added to it. "I hardly know of any experiment that is more adapted to amaze and surprise than this, which exhibits a quantity of air which, as it were, devours a quantity of another kind of air half as large as itself, and yet is so far from gaining any addition to its bulk that it is considerably diminished by it. . . ." [9]

He further observed (a) that although the colorless "nitrous air" was not soluble in water, the red fumes, which we know as nitrogen dioxide (NO_2), were highly water-soluble; (b) that the red fumes were *not* formed when "nitrous air" was mixed with confined air in which a candle had burned until its flame had gone out; and (c) that the diminution in the combined volumes of "nitrous air" and common air varied with the "goodness" of the latter—that is, with the ability to support life and fire. The "better" the air, the greater the reduction of volume. The "best" air could be reduced by one-fifth. The "worst" air was not reduced at all: One volume of "nitrous air" added to two volumes of thoroughly "bad" air produced three volumes of mixture. Evidently (thought Priestley) the formation and dissolving of the red fumes removed from common air that part of it (one-fifth) which was free of phlogiston (dephlogisticated), leaving that which was saturated with phlogiston. Hence, "nitrous air" could be used to test "the goodness of air . . . much more accurately than can be done by putting mice or any other animals to breathe in it." It was this "nitrous air" test which helped Priestley make his greatest discovery.

Meanwhile, he continued to play with his new "air" in the laboratory. When he brought it into contact with metallic iron, he found that "a most remarkable and un-expected change was made" in it. Not only would a candle now burn in it, but also the candle burned with a flame "twice as large as it is naturally, and sometimes not less than five or six times larger." In other words, the action of iron dephlogisticated the "nitrous air," transforming it into what he called "diminished nitrous air," which we know as nitrous oxide (N_2O)—the "laughing gas" whose anesthetizing properties, still made use of for minor surgical operations, were discovered thirty years later by Humphry Davy (1778-1829).

Nor were "nitrous air" and "diminished nitrous air" the only "airs" discovered by Priestley while he was in Leeds. In 1773 he began to use mercury, instead of water, in his pneumatic trough and was enabled to add to his impressive list the discovery of "marine acid air" (hydrogen chloride, HCl); "alkaline air" (ammonia, NH_3); and, in 1774, "vitriolic acid air" (sulfur dioxide, SO_2).

He also applied to his study of "air" the knowledge of electricity he had gained in his earlier work. In 1773 he originated a method of sparking "airs"—that is, passing electric sparks through them—in enclosed glass vessels. In one such experiment he inverted a glass tube of atmospheric air over a trough of water that had been colored blue with litmus and then shot an electric spark through this confined air repeatedly. He observed two effects: The volume of air in the tube was diminished, and the water turned from blue to red. The latter fact indicated that the water had become acidified, for litmus is a substance that is blue in a neutral or alkaline solution but red in an acid one. In another experiment Priestley passed sparks through "alkaline air" (ammonia) and was astonished to find that the volume of the "air" was *increased*. "I . . . observed that every stroke [of electricity] added considerably to the quantity of air; and when water was admitted to it, just so much [of the air] remained unabsorbed as had been added by the explosions."

By the time he moved from Leeds to Calne, in the summer of 1773, his discoveries so crowded upon one another that he decided to send no more papers to the Royal Society on the subject of "air." Doing so might delay the publication of his experiments, and this was "peculiarly unjustifiable" in view of the rapid progress then being made in pneumatic chemistry. He projected instead a multivolumed work entitled *Experiments and Observations on Different Kinds of Air*. The first volume, dedicated to Lord Shelburne, was issued in 1774. Volume II followed in 1775; Volume III, in 1777; Volume IV, in 1779; Volume V, in 1781; and Volume VI (the last of his magnum opus), in 1786.

He announced at the outset his intention to disclose with complete candor not only the methods and results of his experiments but also his views and expectations as each piece of work was done. Hence, *Priestley on Air* (to quote the title stamped on the book's binding) is only slightly less revealing of its author's mind and temperament than it is of his science, the latter being presented with infectious zest as a questing adventure, a voyage of discovery, full of surprises and unexpected twists and turns.

> I do not think it at all degrading to the business of experimental philosophy [he wrote] to compare it ... to the diversion of hunting, when it sometimes happens that those who have beat the ground most, and are consequently the best acquainted with it, weary themselves without starting any game; when it may fall to the way of a mere passenger; so that there is little room for boasting in the most successful termination of the chase.

Another passage, this one from the Preface to Volume I of his masterpiece, might have been aimed directly at Lavoisier, although in fact it was not:

> When, for the sake of a little more reputation, men can keep brooding over a new fact, in the discovery of which they might possibly have very little real merit, until they

think they can astonish the world with a system as complete as it is new, and give mankind a prodigious idea of their judgment and penetration, they are justly punished for their ingratitude to the fountain of all knowledge, and for the want of genuine love of science and of mankind in finding their boasted discoveries anticipated and the field of honest fame pre-occupied by men who, from a natural ardor of mind, engage in philosophical pursuits, and with an ingenuous simplicity immediately communicate to others whatever occurs to them in their inquiries.

Priestley's Great Discovery

It is with Volume II of Priestley's *Experiments and Observations,* particularly with Section III of this volume, that history is chiefly concerned. This section, entitled "Of Dephlogisticated Air, and of the Constitution of the Atmosphere," opened with some self-revealing general remarks:

The contents of this section will furnish a very striking illustration of the truth of a remark which I have more than once made in my philosophical writings, and which can hardly be too often repeated, as it tends greatly to encourage philosophical investigations, viz., that more is owing to what we call *chance*—that is, philosophically speaking, to the observation of *events arising from unknown causes* than to any proper *design* or preconceived *theory* in this business. This does not appear in the works of those who write *synthetically* upon these subjects, but would, I doubt not, appear very strikingly in those who are the most celebrated for their philosophical acumen did they write *analytically* and *ingenuously.*

For my own part, I will frankly acknowledge that at the commencement of the experiments recited in this section I was so far from having formed any hypothesis that led to the discoveries I made in pursuing them that they would have appeared very improbable to me had I been told of them; and when the decisive facts did at length obtrude themselves upon my notice it was very slowly, and with great hesitation, that I yielded to the evidence of my senses. And yet, when I reconsider the matter, and compare my last discoveries relating to the constitution of the atmosphere with the first, I see the closest and easiest connection in the world between them, so as to wonder that I should not have been led immediately from the one to the other. That this was not the case I attribute to the force of prejudice which, unknown to ourselves, biases not only our *judgments,* properly so called, but even the perceptions of our senses; for we may take a maxim so strongly for granted that the plainest evidence of sense will not entirely change, and often hardly modify, our persuasions; and the more ingenious a man is, the more effectually he is entangled in his errors, his ingenuity only helping him to deceive himself by evading the force of truth.

He then recounted the series of "accidents" that led to his discovery of an "air purer than the best common air." The first accident was his procurement of a "burning lens" of greater power than any he had had before—"a lens of twelve inches diameter, and twenty inches focal distance." The "want" of such a lens had theretofore prevented his making "many of the experiments that I had projected, and which...appeared very promising." The second "accident" was that "Mr. Warltire, a good chymist, and lecturer in natural philosophy" happened "to be at that time in Calne." To him Priestley "explained" his views; from him he obtained "many substances, which I could not otherwise have procured." Among these, presumably, was the red calx of mercury (mercuric oxide, HgO), from which he "endeavored to extract air" by heating it with his new burning lens on the hot bright Sunday of August 1, 1774. This sample of the red oxide he called *"mercurius calcinatus per se,"* distinguishing it from the "common

red precipitate" of mercury—the former being obtained by
heating quicksilver in air, the latter by heating mercuric
nitrate, $Hg(NO_3)_2$—although the two (as he did not know)
are of the same chemical composition. He "presently found
that, by means of this lens, air was expelled from it very
readily." After procuring "about three or four times as
much [of this air] as the bulk of my materials" he "admitted
water to it, and found that it was not imbibed by it." The
"air," in other words, did not dissolve in water as "fixed
air" would have done.

> But what surprised me more than I can well express
> [he went on] was that a candle burned in this air with a
> remarkably vigorous flame, very much like that enlarged
> flame with which a candle burns in nitrous air exposed to
> iron or liver of sulphur [that is, nitrous oxide or "laughing
> gas"], but as I had got nothing like this remarkable appear-
> ance from any kind of air besides this particular modifica-
> tion of nitrous air, and I knew no nitrous acid was used in
> the preparation of *mercurius calcinatus,* I was utterly at a
> loss how to account for it.

He also noted that the candle's flame was not only larger
but also hotter and more brilliant than any he had seen
before, "though I did not give sufficient attention to the
circumstance at the time."

Confusion was compounded in his mind by the fact that
simultaneously with the experiment just described:

> [I] extracted a quantity of air with the very same prop-
> erty from the common *red precipitate* which, being pro-
> duced by a solution of mercury in spirit of nitre [nitric
> acid, HNO_3], made me conclude that this peculiar prop-
> erty, being similar to that of the modification of nitrous air
> above mentioned, depended upon something being com-
> municated to it by the nitrous acid; and since the *mercurius
> calcinatus* is produced by exposing mercury to a certain
> degree of heat, where common air has access to it, I like-

wise concluded that this substance had collected something of *nitre,* in that state of heat, from the atmosphere.

Naturally, in these circumstances, he "entertained some suspicion that the *mercurius calcinatus* on which I had made my experiments, being bought at a common apothecary's, might, in fact, be nothing more than the red precipitate." When he mentioned this "suspicion" to Mr. Warltire, however, he was "furnished" with some *mercurius calcinatus* that Warltire had "kept for a specimen of the preparation, and which ... he could warrant to be genuine." He treated this "in the same manner as the former, only by a longer continuance of heat," and "extracted much more air from it than the other."

Nevertheless, a "suspicion" about the purity of his sample remained. It crossed the Channel with him and Lord Shelburne a week or two later, when he and his noble patron set out on a tour of the Continent.

The two men took with them their own cook and carriage, landing in Calais and thence proceeding at a leisurely pace through northern France, Austrian Flanders, Holland ("I can hardly express how very low, beastly, and sordid, the manners of the common people of this country are. . . . Upon the whole, we were much disgusted with the people of Holland. . . ."), and Germany, where they went up the Rhine as far as Strasbourg. They spent October, 1774, in Paris, which impressed Priestley unfavorably despite the effective spirit of liberal reform that had followed the unmourned death of Louis XV and his succession by young Louis XVI in May of that year. Admitting "the spaciousness and magnificence of the public buildings," he was "exceedingly offended with the narrowness, dirt, and stench, of almost all the streets." He was also put out by the irreligion that prevailed among the brilliant Parisian men of science and letters to whom, as a distinguished foreign philosopher, he was of course introduced and by whom he was entertained. "I am here in the midst of unbelievers, and even Atheists," he complained in a letter to an English friend. "I had a long conversation with one, an ingenious man, and good writer, who maintained seriously that man might arise, with any Maker, from the earth. They may despise me; I am sure I despise them."

During this memorable month Priestley met for the first and last times Antoine Lavoisier, who showed him his laboratory and had him to dinner at least once at the small mansion in the Rue Neuve-des-Bons-Enfants. There he met Mme. Lavoisier. There he told the assembled company of the mysterious new "air" produced by his intense heating of the mercury calx and of the questions concerning it, which he hoped to answer through further inquiries. There, too, he heard of some experiments with the mercury calx that had been reported the preceding February by the French chemist Pierre Bayen (1725-98). Like Priestley, Bayen had transformed calx into metal by heating it *in the absence* of the charcoal which, according to the phlogiston theory, was needed for such a transformation, but unlike Priestley, Bayen had paid little, if any, attention to the "air" emitted in the process. He identified it (ludicrously wide of the mark) as "fixed air"!

Priestley in Paris "did not omit the opportunity . . . to get an ounce of *mercurius calcinatus* prepared by Mr. Cadet [Antoine Cadet de Vaux], of the genuineness of which there could not possibly be any suspicion." He carried it with him as a precious part of his baggage when he returned to England in November, leaving Lord Shelburne behind. "I am quite tired of the idleness in which I spend my time here," he had written in a letter from Paris, "and long exceedingly to be about my experiments."

Having returned to Calne, he at once "went to work

upon the *mercurius calcinatus* which I had procured from Mr. Cadet" and found that it behaved in the same way as his earlier samples from Warltire. It produced the same mysterious "air." He was soon convinced that this air was *not* "modified nitrous air" (nitrous oxide), despite "their resemblance in some particulars."

> [W]hat I observed new at this time [Nov. 19] . . . was, that, whereas a few moments agitation in water will deprive the modified nitrous air of its property of admitting a candle to burn in it; yet, after more than ten times as much agitation as would be sufficient to produce this alteration in the nitrous air, no sensible change was produced in this. A candle still burned in it with a strong flame; and it did not, in the least, diminish common air, which I have observed that nitrous air, in this state, in some measure, does.

The obvious next step was to measure the "goodness" of the calx-derived air with the "nitrous air" test. Priestley, however, did not take this step until March 1, 1775, "having, in the mean time, been intent upon my experiments with vitriolic acid air . . . and the various modifications of air produced by spirit of nitre. . . ." He then put "one measure of nitrous air to two measures of" the calx-derived air and found "that it was diminished quite as much as common air." On the same day he applied the same test to air he had extracted from red lead (he had discovered the preceding August that red lead could be made to yield apparently the same kind of air as the red calx of mercury), achieving the same result. His conclusion was that both red lead and the mercury calx yielded common atmospheric air, if a "better" sample of it than he had ever obtained before.

Then came the crucial "accident."

When he left the laboratory on the evening of March 1,

he left standing the "mixture of nitrous air and the air from *mercurius calcinatus*." It stood all night, "in which time the whole diminution must have taken place; and, consequently, had it been common air, it must have been perfectly noxious, and entirely unfit for respiration or inflammation." He was therefore astonished on the morning of March 2, when on a sudden impulse he thrust a lighted candle into the enclosed air and found that the candle burned in it "even better than in common air." He wrote: "I cannot, at this distance of time, recollect what it was I had in view in making this experiment; but I know I had no expectation of the real issue of it. . . . If . . . I had not happened, for some other purpose, to have had a lighted candle before me, I should probably never have made the trial. . . ."

Even then, although he considered it "something very extraordinary," he had "no conception of the real cause of this phenomenon." So imbued was his mind with the conception of atmospheric air as a single elemental substance containing various degrees and kinds of "impurities" that he simply could not admit the possibility of there being an air "better" (more completely *dephlogisticated*) than the "best" common air. Hence, he continued to believe that the new air he had tested was "substantially the same thing with common air." "I particularly remember my telling Dr. Price," he wrote, "that I was myself perfectly satisfied of its being common air, as it appeared to be so by the test of nitrous air; though, for the satisfaction of others, I wanted a mouse to make the proof complete."

But his attempt "to make the proof complete" resulted (as often happens) in a complete disproof of this thesis. On March 8, having procured a full-grown mouse, he "put it into a glass vessel containing two ounce-measures of the air from *mercurius calcinatus*." Had this been common air, the mouse would have lived in it "about fifteen minutes."

As it was, the mouse "lived a full half hour; and though it was taken out seemingly dead, it appeared to have been only exceedingly chilled; for, upon being held to the fire, it presently revived, and appeared not to have received any harm from the experiment." There then definitely entered his mind for the first time the "suspicion" that the calx-derived air might have as distinct and separate an identity as others he had discovered. He acted on this suspicion the following day, March 9, applying his "nitrous air" test to the air the mouse had breathed. The familiar "red fumes" were formed, and the total volume of air was diminished —diminished, indeed, to such an extent as to prove that the tested air, "though it had been breathed so long, . . . was still better than common air." He went on:

> For after mixing it with nitrous air, in the usual pro-
> portion to two to one, it was diminished in the proportion
> of $4\frac{1}{2}$ to $3\frac{1}{2}$; that is, the nitrous air had made it two
> ninths less than before, and this in a very short space of
> time; whereas I had never found that, in the longest time,
> any common air was reduced more than one fifth of its
> bulk by any proportion of nitrous air. . . . Thinking of this
> extraordinary fact upon my pillow, the next morning I
> put another measure of nitrous air to the same mixture,
> and, to my utter astonishment, found that it was further
> diminished to almost one half of its original quantity.

Subsequently, working with samples derived from red lead, as well as from the mercury calx, he found that whereas "common air takes about one-half of its bulk from nitrous air before it begins to receive any addition to its dimensions from more nitrous air," the amazing *new* air "took more than four half-measures before it ceased to be diminished by more nitrous air, and even five half-measures made no addition to the original dimensions."

He now clearly saw where he had been led astray by his

earlier observations. When he had first tested the new air with "nitrous air," he had been "so fully possessed by the notion of there being no air better than common air" that he had failed to notice "that the redness [of the red fumes] was really deeper, and the diminution [of total volume] something greater than common air would have admitted." As a matter of fact and as repeated experiments now showed, a mixture of 1 volume of "nitrous air" with 2 of the new air resulted in a diminution of the 3 volumes to 1.6 volumes, instead of the 1.8 volumes that remained in the case of the best common air.

Priestley could no longer doubt that he had discovered a "new species of air," one more completely *dephlogisticated,* hence more capable of absorbing phlogiston (supporting fire and breathing), than any that had been known before. He had discovered what we now know as "oxygen" —the name later given it by Lavoisier. Priestley, in the letter he wrote to Sir John Pringle, President of the Royal Society, on March 15, 1775, announcing his discovery, called it dephlogisticated air, and he would continue so to call it to the end of his days. Two months later, on May 24, 1775, he wrote Pringle that he had now been able to produce "dephlogisticated air" by treating various "earths" with nitric acid. "Upon the whole," he wrote in this letter, "I think it may be safely concluded, that the purest air is that which contains the least *phlogiston:* that air is impure (by which I mean that it is unfit for respiration and for the purpose of supporting flame) in proportion as it contains more of that principle. . . ."

In 1772, about three years before Priestley completed the experiments just described, the great Swedish chemist Karl Wilhelm Scheele (1742-86) launched a carefully planned series of investigations having to do, initially, with the reaction between metallic iron and common air.

He soon succeeded in isolating oxygen, obtaining it from the black oxide of manganese (reacting with sulfuric acid), as well as later from the red calx of mercury. He described its unique properties in unmistakable terms and named it "fire air" in a book (his only book) entitled, in English, *Fire and Air*. The completed manuscript of this work was delivered to the printer at about the time Priestley was at last disabusing himself of the notion that what he had been observing was common air. The Swedish printer, however, was unforgivably dilatory: He did not bring out the book until 1777, two years too late for Scheele's discovery to be an effective influence on the work of other men.

4. *Lavoisier the Systematizer*

Birth Pains of a Theory

The conclusions Lavoisier finally reached concerning the combustion of diamonds derived not only from the two sets of experiments he made with them, in August, 1772, and October, 1773, but also from certain experiments he made with phosphorus and sulfur in September and October, 1772, and from yet other experiments which initiated a connected series in early 1773.

His first experiment with phosphorus was made on September 10, 1772, according to a fragmentary note in his laboratory book. The note said that he had purchased from M. Mitouard "an ounce of good German phosphorus for 45 louis cost of manufacture" and had put a small piece of it in a bottle where it "became luminous" and "fumed without becoming hot." When he brought the bottle "near the fire," the phosphorus "was instantly kindled with crackling," although the bottle remained unbroken. Then came the key sentence, the germ of a revolutionary idea:

"Emboldened by this success, I wanted to find out in the same apparatus *whether phosphorus absorbed air in burning* [our italics]." By October 20, 1772, his experiments had convinced him that phosphorus did indeed absorb air in burning and was thereby increased in weight. They had not, however, caused him to doubt the phlogiston theory; his report spoke of the combustion of phosphorus as a process in which the "phosphorus is decomposed" and the "phlogiston leaves it."

Four or five days later he was convinced by experiment that the same thing happened with sulfur and "may well take place in the case of all substances that gain in weight by combustion and calcination." (The quotation is from the sealed note he left with the secretary of the Academy of Science in November, 1772.) The note went on:

> I have carried out the reduction of litharge [lead monoxide, PbO] in closed vessels, with the apparatus of Hales [the pneumatic trough], and I observed that, just as the calx changed into metal, a large quantity of air was liberated and that this air formed a volume a thousand times greater than the quantity of litharge employed. This discovery appearing to me one of the most interesting of those that have been made since the time of Stahl, I felt that I ought to secure my right to it, by depositing this note in the hands of the Secretary of the Academy, to remain sealed until the time when I shall make my experiments known. Paris, November 1, 1772. Lavoisier.

He had caught his first glimpses of a common denominator of hitherto separate and distinct chemical phenomena, a pattern whereby these might be meaningfully related to one another, and his excitement was evident.

Nearly four months later, on February 20, 1773, he addressed to himself in his laboratory notebook a memorandum, saying in part:

Before commencing a long series of experiments that I intend to make on the elastic fluid that is set free from substances, either by fermentation, or distillation or in every kind of chemical change, and also on the air absorbed in the combustion of a great many substances, I feel impelled to set down here some considerations in writing, in order to outline for myself the course I ought to take. ... It is certain that there is liberated from substances, under a great many conditions, an elastic fluid; but there are in existence several doctrines as to its nature. Some, like Mr. Hales and his adherents, deemed that this substance was the air itself, of the atmosphere. ... He thought that the elastic fluid cannot differ from that which we breathe, except in its being more loaded with matters that may be harmful or healthful. ... Some scientific men, coming after Mr. Hales, observed differences so great between the air liberated from substances and that which we breathe, that they deemed it to be another substance, to which they have given the name of fixed air. ... A third class of scientific men were of the opinion that the elastic matter which escapes from substances was different according to the substances from which it was derived, and their conclusion was that it was not other than an emanation of the minute and ultimate parts of substances, of which one could distinguish innumerable kinds. ... These differences [in doctrine] will be exhibited in their full extent when I ... give the history of all that has been done on the air that is liberated from substances and that combines with them. The importance of the end in view prompted me to undertake all this work, which seemed to me destined to bring about a revolution in physics and chemistry. I have felt bound to look upon all that has been done before me as merely suggestive: I have proposed to repeat it all with new safeguards, in order to link our knowledge of the air that goes into combustion or that is liberated from substances, with other acquired knowledge, and to form a theory.

Nowhere in the memorandum does the word "phlogiston" occur.

There followed months of intense work in his library and laboratory. He read omnivorously—sometimes inaccurately—the works of Boyle, Hales, Black, Cavendish, Priestley, and many lesser lights. He conducted a swift series of experiments in which metals were calcined and calxes reduced to metals, careful attention being in each case paid to the weight changes that occurred in these processes and to the relationship between these changes and the absorption or production of air. An excess of ambition and a deficiency of patience drove and marred what was, nevertheless, a work amazing in quantity and scarcely less so in quality, although the latter was certainly uneven. By May 5, 1773, he felt sufficiently sure of the correctness of his basic assumptions to request that his sealed note be opened and read to the Academy. By midautumn he had completed and sent to the printer the book in which he was to publish his experiments to the world and inaugurate (he hoped) his scientific "revolution." By December 7 the book had been submitted to the Academy and reviewed, ostensibly by a committee of four appointed for the purpose. (Something of Lavoisier's character is revealed by the fact that he himself was evidently the real author of the favorable review which this committee issued and that the review emphasized the "rigorous method" of weights and measures with which "M. Lavoisier has tested all his results" rather than the theoretical interpretation of these results. He was having difficulty with the latter.) In January, 1774, the book was published, with the title *Opuscules physiques et chimiques* ("Essays in Physics and Chemistry"), complimentary copies being dispatched to Franklin, Priestley, Black, and Scheele, among others.

To at least some of the recipients, including Priestley, it was at once evident that Lavoisier the theoretician had considerably outrun Lavoisier the experimenter in the composition of the *Opuscules*. In general, the theoretical conclusions lacked adequate experimental support, the experiments being for the most part repetitions of work done (sometimes better done) by others. They discovered no important new facts. For instance, Lavoisier concluded at one point:

> Several circumstances would seem to lead to the belief, that the whole of the air which we breathe is not adapted to be fixed, and enter into combination with metallic calces; but that there exists in the atmosphere an elastic fluid [that is, a gas] of a particular kind which is mixed with the air, and that it is at the instant that the quantity of this fluid contained under the receiver is consumed, that the calcination can no longer take place.

His only laboratory evidence for this was a single experiment in which the enclosed atmospheric air was diminished by a mere 5 percent when calcination of the enclosed metal (it was lead) ceased at the focal point of the burning glass. We now know that the diminution, in a properly conducted experiment, should have approximated 20 percent, the percentage of the atmosphere composed of oxygen. Priestley, in an experiment published before Lavoisier conducted his, had come much nearer the mark, noting a diminution in air volume of between one-fifth and one-fourth. (When the great discrepancy between his experimental result and Priestley's was later called to his attention, Lavoisier suggested that it might be accounted for by variations at different times and places in the amount of "fixable elastic fluid" in the air!)

In regard to general theory, Lavoisier in this book maintained with unyielding consistency that the weight increase occurring during the calcination of metals was due to something taken from the air and combined with the metal, and it is evident that he was increasingly inclined to regard phlogiston as a needless complication, if not flatly contradictory of a true description of the combustion process. He refrained from any direct attack on the phlogiston doctrine, but he made clear his view that a metallic calx, far from being a simpler substance than the metal, as the phlogiston doctrine asserted, was in fact more complex. It consisted, not of a metal *minus* something, but of a metal *plus* something—something taken from the air. As for what this "something" was, however, he was notably vague, wavering, even self-contradictory. For the most part he supposed that it was "fixed air"—despite the disturbing fact that "fixed air" extinguished flames and smothered animals. On one occasion he implied that the "something" was atmospheric air itself, as a whole; on another, that it was a particular (unidentified) "elastic fluid" *contained* in atmospheric air; and on yet another, that it was an integral part (although the "heavier part") of atmospheric air. Obviously he could not decide whether atmospheric air was a homogeneous elemental substance, as most chemists continued to believe, or an alterable mixture of different kinds of air, as the discoveries of Black, Cavendish, and Priestley seemed to indicate.

At one point in this book Lavoisier referred to some work that Boyle had published in the *Essay on Effluviams* a century before. Observing the weight increase accompanying the calcination of metals, Boyle explained it as the absorption by the metal of material particles of fire. These particles were so infinitesimal that they could pass through the pores of glass; this explained why the weight increase occurred even when metals were calcined in sealed vessels—an experiment Boyle himself performed. Lavoisier's explanation, as we have seen, was very different. At the end of Chapter VI of the *Opuscules* he asserted: "1st, That the calcination of metals cannot take place in vessels closely stopped, or, at least, that it can only be in proportion to the air which is confined in them: 2dly, That in case the calcination could proceed in vessels closely stopped and exhausted of air, it should then be without increase of weight, and consequently with circumstances very different from those observed in calcination performed in air." When he wrote these lines, they were in the nature of a surmise. He had not performed experiments that would verify or disprove them. He proceeded to do so soon after his book had been published.

If Boyle's explanation was valid, argued Lavoisier, a sealed vessel containing the calcined metal must weigh more than the same vessel before calcination had taken place, the difference being accounted for by the absorption of particles from outside the vessel. Accordingly, he weighed on his highly sensitive balance several samples of tin (in small pieces) and of lead, placing them in glass retorts of various sizes, which he then sealed airtight and carefully weighed before heating them slowly on a charcoal furnace until the metal was in what he called a state of complete fusion. (This part of the experiment he performed wearing a mask and goggles to protect himself from flying glass, for Boyle had warned that when heated, the vessels tended to explode "with a noise like the Report of a Gun.") He maintained the metal at maximum heat for two hours, observing that more calx was formed in the larger than in the smaller retorts—this was what he expected—and that calcination appeared to cease in the largest retorts after one hour. Having cooled the retorts, he weighed them, still sealed, and found (or reported that he found) that they weighed *exactly* the same as before heating. Very carefully, then, he punctured the seals and listened with satisfaction to the whistle of air rushing *into* the vessels—a whistle that was, he reported, "higher [in pitch], louder, and longer" for the larger than for the smaller vessels. Again he resorted to the balance and found that following the reentry of air, each retort increased in weight to an amount roughly proportionate to the vessel's size and exactly the same as the weight increase that was found to have occurred when he weighed the metal calxes separately. He had conclusively demonstrated, he reported in a memoir submitted to the Academy on April 14, 1774, that:

> ... the increase in weight of metals calcined in sealed vessels comes neither from the matter of fire nor from any matter outside the retort, but it is from the air contained in the vessel that the metal takes the substance that increases its weight and converts it into calx; and that what deceived Boyle was this, that in all his experiments he neglected to weigh the vessel before opening it and he had attributed to the matter of fire an increase of weight that actually came from that part of the external air that entered the vessel.

But what was this "substance" that came out of the air? He still had no clear idea. He was at this stage in the development of his theory when he met Priestley.

Priestley Supplies the Missing Piece

The Lavoisiers entertained Priestley and a group of the most distinguished Parisian philosophers, including the chemists Pierre Macquer, Le Roy, and Cadet de Vaux, on an evening in October, 1774. Already Priestley had visited Lavoisier's laboratory, where, as he was soon to write, "I saw with great astonishment the rapid production of, I believe, near two gallons of air from a mixture of spirits of niter and spirit of wine ... and when that ingenious philosopher applied the flame of a candle ... it burned with a blue flame. ..." Actually he had not been much impressed with Lavoisier's experimental studies thus far—

the Frenchman was a mere beginner in pneumatic chemistry, after all—but he *had* been impressed by Lavoisier's laboratory equipment and had formed a high opinion of Lavoisier's abilities. "The world has great expectations of him and I doubt not that he will abundantly answer them," he wrote later to Lavoisier's great and good friend Trudaine de Montigny, and if there is a touch of condescension in this, there is also a faint echo of the flattery he felt at the younger man's deference to him. The whole visit had been and continued to be, on the surface, most amicable.

Underneath, however, half realized by each, there had been uneasiness. Priestley had certain reservations concerning his host's character. He disapproved of what struck him as vainglory and conceit—a streak of them anyway—linked with a desire to astonish and overawe and with a carelessness of the rights of other people. He himself was "determined" in his writings "to show how little *mystery* there really is in the business of experimental philosophy, and with how little *sagacity,* or even *design,* discoveries (which some persons are pleased to consider as great and wonderful things) have been made." He was always scrupulously accurate in his statements of other men's works and views and of his debts to them. Not so with Lavoisier. For instance, in the first part of the *Opuscules* the Frenchman had (as Priestley wrote later) "undertaken to give a pretty full account of all that has been done before him in the same way," but his statements of Priestley's alleged views were so inaccurate as to amount to outright falsification in several instances. Priestley was to use four pages of an Appendix to Volume II of his *Experiments and Observations* to print in parallel columns "Mr. Lavoisier's Account of my Experiments and Observations" and "The true Account of them."

This, however, was in the future. He sat now at Mme.

Lavoisier's right hand—a plain man in sober garb, rubbing his large nose from time to time and squinting his eyes in an effort to understand a language foreign to him and spoken (he thought) much too rapidly. He was thankful that the slender, pretty, animated Mme. Lavoisier addressed him in English and was impressed by the fact that she, at only seventeen, had established herself as an equal in this brilliant company.

The others talked, too. He was further confirmed in an opinion he had just expressed in a letter home: "In general the French are too much taken up with themselves to admit of that minute and benevolent attention to others which is essential in politeness. This appears in nothing more than their continually interrupting one another in discourse, which they do without the least apology so that one half the persons in company are heard talking at the same time." He spoke as some one who still stammered badly on occasion and who resented now and then, while envying always, the glibness of others.

There was one point in the evening, however, when he found the whole table listening with close attention to his words. He spoke then in his imperfect French about the remarkable "species of air" (was it "modified nitrous air"?) which he had derived from the red calx of mercury and from what he called *plombe rouge. Plombe rouge?* His listeners were puzzled. At last old Macquer understood that what the Englishman referred to was "minium," or red lead. Then, as Priestley later wrote, "all the company, and Mr. and Mrs. Lavoisier as much as any, expressed great surprise."

The probability is high that Lavoisier's personal attitude toward Priestley, the attitude that was further defined in the months following the Englishman's return to Calne, was a mingling of respect, envy, and contempt. Priestley's

experimental skill commanded respect. His swiftly growing list of important factual discoveries aroused envy. His
seemingly childlike naïveté and his continuous "giving
away" of himself in ways that exposed him needlessly to
the malice of others evoked contempt. But the contempt,
if Lavoisier indeed felt it, was not pure. In Priestley's
crediting of his successes to "chance," rather than to his
own genius and in his insistence on publishing to the world
every stupidity and clumsiness that delayed his progress,
there were manifest a selflessness, humility, and candid
truthfulness whose recognition by the impatient and ambitious young Frenchman would have constituted a rebuke
of himself. For Lavoisier lacked to a degree the moral
integrity of this plain, simple, stammering Englishman.
He was neither as scrupulous nor as benevolent of motive
as Priestley. There was in him a still unresolved conflict
between willful selfishness and ideal commitment, and if
the latter eventually prevailed, it was in part because of
pressures outside himself.

The first memoir of Lavoisier's experiments with sealed
vessels, read at a public meeting of the Academy on November 12, 1774, indicated that his conclusions derived from
a number of successful experiments with tin and lead,
whereas in fact most of his sealed retorts had blown up:
He had actually completed two conclusive experiments
with tin and, as he later confessed, "hardly one for lead."
Moreover, his memoir stated that the sealed retorts,
weighed "with the most scrupulous attention," were always
precisely the same weight before and after heating and that
the increase in the vessel's weight after the seal was broken
was "always exactly equal" to the increase in the weight of
the metal. In fact, there was a slight decrease in the weight
of each sealed retort immediately following its heating,
and when he permitted one of them to stand sealed over-
night, he noted a *gain* of weight over that which he had

recorded before calcination began. This was due to the film of moisture that invariably forms on cool glass in atmospheric air, is driven off when the glass is heated, and re-forms as the glass again cools. Of this fact Lavoisier had no knowledge.

He found himself in embarrassing difficulties when this memoir was read abroad in the late summer or early autumn of 1774. He had made clear his belief that he was the first person to discover that air is involved in calcination but was very promptly disabused of that notion. Father Beccaria, the Italian physicist, wrote to inform him that he, Beccaria, had conducted almost precisely these same experiments a full fifteen years before, finding that the degree of calcination was proportionate to the volume of the vessel and that the total weight of each vessel remained the same before and after heating. Moreover, the experiments had been published; Lavoisier might see a reference to them in Volume II of the memoirs of the Turin Academy. The Frenchman was chagrined. His memoir was already in the hands of Abbé Rozier, editor of *Observations sur la Physique, sur l'Histoire Naturelle et sur les Arts* ("Observations on Physics, Natural History, and the Arts"; Rozier's periodical is hereafter designated as Rozier's *Journal*). To Rozier he at once sent a letter enclosing relevant extracts from Beccaria's communication and from the Turin Academy publication, asking that they be printed, if possible, on the page following his own paper. He admitted that, unknown to him, his theory and experiments had been anticipated.

Indeed it soon appeared that the anticipation was farther back in time than he then suspected. Pierre Bayen, whose work with the mercury calx was gracelessly ignored by Lavoisier in his public reading of November 12, 1774, published in Rozier's *Journal* for January, 1775, a letter calling attention to a book by the French scientist Jean

Rey, published in 1630, wherein Rey had explained the weight increase of metallic calxes as resulting from the adherence to them of air that had become "thicker" as a result of heating.* Bayen was proud that "it was a Frenchman who by the power of his genius . . . first divined the cause of the gain in weight shown by certain metals when exposed to the action of fire and converted into calxes; and this cause was precisely the same as that the truth of which . . . [has] just been proved by the experiments described by M. Lavoisier at the last public séance of the Academy of Sciences." Of course, Rey's explanation was *not* just the same as Lavoisier's, but it was sufficiently similar to detract from Lavoisier's claim to complete originality.

One might expect these experiences to restrain the young Frenchman's tendency to claim more credit than was his due; to some extent they may have done so. They did not, however, destroy it.

A few days after the dinner party for Priestley, Lavoisier and Mme. Lavoisier paid their annual visit to the château of Trudaine de Montigny, where on October 28 he repeated Priestley's experiments, with Trudaine assisting, collecting what appeared to be, as Priestley had surmised, "diminished nitrous air." Certainly it was not "fixed air." This was further confirmed in Paris, in November, where Lavoisier worked with a sample of the red calx of mercury that came from the very same bottle that had supplied Priestley. Then, like Priestley in England, he turned his attention to other problems. He returned to experiments with the new air on March 1, 1775—the very day that Priestley, at Calne, was for the first time applying his "nitrous air" test to what he would soon identify as "dephlogisticated air."

It was during the immediately following weeks that Lavoisier made one of his most famous experiments, re-

* See footnote, p. 99.

peating it (he said) "many times," the last of them on March 31, 1775, "in the presence of . . . the Duc de la Rochefoucauld, and MM. Trudaine de Montigny, Macquer, and Cadet." He employed apparatus of his own devising, wherein Priestley's improvements of Hales' pneumatic trough were embodied.

Lavoisier's apparatus for experiments with the calcination of metals. A burning lens focused on the metal to be heated.

His first step was an independent verification of experimental results already obtained by Bayen, whose work, however, he was again to refrain from mentioning when he made his report. He used his apparatus to make certain "that *mercurius calcinatus per se*" was a "true metallic calx," as Bayen's work had indicated it to be. He did this by mixing 1 ounce of the calx with "48 grains of powdered

charcoal" or "to use the accepted expression [whose validity he now doubted] by the addition of phlogiston" in his
retort, which he then heated. In "not ... more than three-
quarters of an hour" all the calx was "reduced" to pure
mercury and "the air" had "ceased rising." He found that
"the quantity of air set free amounted to 64 cubic inches,
without allowing for the volume necessarily absorbed in
passing through water," and that when "submitted ... to
a large number of tests," it manifested "precisely the qualities of the kind of air known as fixed air or mephitic air
such as is obtained from all metallic calxes by the addition
of charcoal [and] ... is set free from fermenting matters."
Hence, it was "unquestionable that *mercurius calcinatus
per se* should be included in the category of metallic
calxes."

His second and final step was:

> ... to examine this calx alone, to reduce it without addi-
> tion [*i.e.,* without the charcoal that was deemed to be virtu-
> ally pure phlogiston], to see if some air would be set free,
> and if so, to determine what state it was in. To accomplish
> this, [I] put into a retort of the same size as before one
> ounce of *mercurius calcinatus per se* alone; I arranged the
> apparatus in the same way as for the preceding experi-
> ment, so that all the circumstances were exactly the same;
> the reduction was a little more difficult than with the addi-
> tion of charcoal; it required more heat and there was no
> perceptible effect till the retort began to get slightly red-
> hot; then air was set free little by little, and passed into the
> bell-jar, and the same degree of heat being maintained for
> $2\frac{1}{2}$ hours, all the *mercurius calcinatus per se* was reduced.

On the Parisian weight scale he was using, 1 ounce contained 576 grains, and when the "operation" was "completed," he found that the 576 grains of calx originally
placed in the retort had been "reduced" to 522 grains of

liquid mercury, a net loss of 54 grains of solid matter. Simultaneously there had been "set free" and collected above the water in the bell jar 78 cubic inches of air. If it were assumed that the 54 grains of solid calx had been transformed into 78 cubic inches of air, "then each cubic inch [of air] must weigh a little less than two-thirds of a grain, which does not differ much from the weight of ordinary air."

Actually, as James Bryant Conant pointed out in Case 2 of the *Harvard Case Studies in Experimental Science,* the weight difference was considerable by Lavoisier's own account. In the *Opuscules* he had said that 1 cubic inch of atmospheric air, at the usual temperature and pressure of a laboratory, weighed 0.46 grain, or 36/78 of a grain compared with the 54/78 he calculated (very roughly) for the air now collected in his bell jar. "Therefore," said Conant, "his statement . . . is an optimistic statement by an investigator looking for an agreement between two numbers."[1] Lavoisier wanted his new air to weigh the same, or nearly the same, as atmospheric air because he was in the process of identifying it as an unusually "pure" or "good" sample of such air—the same identification Priestley had once made and was now abandoning. He promptly submitted "the 78 cubic inches of air I had obtained to all the tests suitable for determining its nature" and found much to his surprise that it did not dissolve in water, did not precipitate limewater, did not combine "with fixed or volatile alkalis" or "at all diminish their caustic qualities," could "be used again for the calcination of metals," was "diminished like common air by an addition of a third of nitrous air," and, "finally," had "none of the properties of fixed air." On the positive side, the new air seemed "more suited to support" the "respiration" of animals and the burning of candles than

common air. The candle flames increased "in a very remarkable manner and . . . [gave] much more light than in
common air."

All these quotations are from what has become famous
in the history of science as the "Easter Memoir of Lavoisier," read before the Academy at its Easter *rentrée publique* on April 26, 1775. His own title was *Mémoire sur
la nature du principe qui se combine avec les Métaux
pendant leur calcination, et qui en augmente le poids*
("Memoir on the Nature of the Principle Which Combines
With Metals During Calcination and Increases Their
Weight"). By "principle" he meant, obviously, "substance"
or "element." He opened:

> Are there different kinds of air? Does it suffice that a
> body should be in a state of permanent elasticity in order
> to be considered a kind of air? Are the different airs that
> nature offers us, or that we succeed in making, exceptional
> substances or modifications of atmospheric air? Such are
> the principal questions embraced in the plan I have formed
> and the problems which I propose to develop before the
> Academy. But . . . I will confine myself today to one par-
> ticular case, and will limit myself to showing that the prin-
> ciple which unites with metals during calcination, which
> increases their weight, and which is a constituent of the
> calx is neither one of the constituent parts of the air, nor
> a particular acid distributed in the atmosphere, that it is
> the air itself entire without alteration, without decomposi-
> tion even to the point that if one sets it free after it has
> been so combined it comes out more pure, more respirable,
> if this expression may be permitted, than the air of the
> atmosphere and is more suitable to support ignition and
> combustion.

Having recounted the experiments spoken of above, he
reiterated that they "proved" the "principle" he had
sought to be "nothing else than the purest part of the

very air which surrounds us" * and which, in the formation of calxes, "passes from a condition of elasticity to
that of solidity; if then it is obtained in the form of fixed
air in all the metallic reductions in which charcoal is used,
this effect is due to the charcoal itself, and it is very likely
that all metallic calxes, like that of mercury, would give
only common air if they could all be reduced without addition [of charcoal] like *mercurius calcinatus per se."*

He concluded:

> From the fact that common air changes to fixed air when
> combined with charcoal it would seem natural to conclude
> that fixed air is nothing but a combination of common air
> and phlogiston. This is Mr. Priestley's opinion and it must
> be admitted that it is not without probability; however,
> when one looks into the facts in detail, contradictions arise
> so frequently I feel it necessary to ask natural philosophers
> and chemists still to suspend judgment; I hope to be soon
> in a position to communicate the reasons for my doubts.

The memoir was published in the May, 1775, issue of
Rozier's *Journal.* Priestley read it there—and with rising
indignation. The brash young Frenchman made no mention whatever of the fact that he had been told—and in
considerable detail—of Priestley's own earlier experiments
with the mercury calx and with red lead. On the contrary,
Lavoisier claimed to have found "much to my surprise"
that the evolved air was not fixed air; in point of fact, he
must have expected to find precisely what he *did* find,
since Priestley had indicated that he would. In the whole
paper Priestley's name was mentioned just once—and then
it was to ascribe to him an "opinion" he did not in fact
hold! "The most unaccountable mistake concerning any
of my opinions relating to air, is that I should be supposed

---

* This seems to contradict his statement that it is the "air entire," but he
obviously means here common air that is wholly divested of impurities.

to maintain that *fixed air is a combination of common air and phlogiston,"* the Englishman protested in the Section XVI he promptly added to Volume II of his *Experiments and Observations,* which he was then preparing for the press.

> This, indeed, is the opinion of Dr. Rutherford ..., of an English Chymist, who probably had it from him, and that of other philosophers in this country, who may have adopted it from them; but every thing that is English is not mine. I have mistakes enow of my own to answer for, and I cannot conceive how any thing that I have ever advanced on the subject should have been construed to bear that meaning.... [S]o far am I from supposing that fixed air is a compound of common air and phlogiston, that, on the other hand, I have always rather considered fixed air as an elementary substance, and common air as a compound.

One may imagine the pleasure that Priestley then took (although he was the least malicious of men) in pointing out to the world the mistake Lavoisier had made on the nature of the calx-derived air:

> [I]t appears ... that, after I left Paris, where I procured the *mercurius calcinatus* above mentioned, and had spoken of the experiments that I had made, and I intended to make with it, he began his experiments upon the same substance, and presently found what I have called *dephlogisticated air,* but without investigating the nature of it. ... For he had only tried it with one-third of nitrous air and observed that a candle burned in it with more vigour than in common air; and though he says it *seems to be* more fit for respiration than common air, he does not say that he had made any trial how long an animal could live in it.... He therefore inferred, as I have said that I myself had once done, that this substance had, during the process of calcination, imbibed atmospheric air, not in part, but in whole.

As for Lavoisier's conclusion that he had found the general "principle" which "combines with metals during calcination," Priestley rejected it as unproved. The fact that the mercury calx yielded fixed air when heated "with addition" (of charcoal), and "dephlogisticated air" when heated alone was no sufficient basis for Lavoisier's conclusion that *all* metallic calxes would "probably" behave in the same way. So said Priestley. The assertion by the Frenchman that the "fixed air" yielded by most calxes when heated with charcoal came from the charcoal was contradicted, Priestley indicated, by his own experiments "in the course of [which] . . . several of those calces yielded fixed air by *heat only,* without any addition of charcoal." (These Priestley experiments would indeed have been a blow against Lavoisier's developing theory, had the conclusion Priestley drew from it been true. But the metallic calxes that yielded "fixed air" when heated alone were impure; they contained carbonates of which the carbon combined with oxygen upon heating to form carbon dioxide [fixed air].) In regard to Lavoisier's request that scientists "suspend judgment" on the conclusion "that fixed air is . . . a combination of common air and phlogiston" until he, Lavoisier, was able to explain why he "doubts" this conclusion, Priestley's comment was (for him) acid. "I, for one, am waiting with some impatience for this explanation," he wrote. Its probable nature being already indicated, Priestley was already prepared to reject it.

There is no record of Lavoisier's personal reaction to Priestley's rebuke. But soon after the Volume II of Priestley's *Experiments and Observations* had come into his hands, the Frenchman began carefully repeating Priestley's experiments with the calx-derived air, this time testing the air carefully. He found Priestley was right. He then devised further experiments, in which, characteristically, he made careful use of the scales to determine the nature of the chemical changes involved. Some of these experiments gave a belated verification to the conclusions he had already announced in his memoir on the calcination of tin and lead in sealed vessels—the memoir first read before the Academy on November 12, 1774—and this he carefully revised to indicate that he now thought of common air as consisting of two distinct parts, one heavier than the other. It was the heavier part that combined with the metal during calcination. He further confessed, as if Priestley's little lecture on the ethics and proper manners of science had had some effect, that the experiments from which he derived his conclusions ought to have been more numerous and various than they in fact were but that they were so difficult, so exacting that he had not "as yet had the courage to extend his researches." Moreover (again Priestley's discovery was having its effect), he was now convinced that this heavier part of the common air that combined with metals was also the "salubrious part," the remainder being incapable of supporting combustion or respiration. The purest common air, in other words, was not a simple element, but a mixture of two radically different "elastic fluids."

He also revised and corrected his "Easter Memoir." When he presented the revised version to a *rentrée publique* of the Academy on August 8, 1778, the "principle" which combined with metals to increase their weight was no longer, in his opening paragraph, "the air itself entire without alteration," but "nothing else than the healthiest and purest part of the air." * In his closing paragraph, it was "the eminently respirable portion of the air." In this paragraph he no longer merely doubted that "fixed air is

* This time he used "part" as an equivalent of "principle," indicating that common air was a mixture.

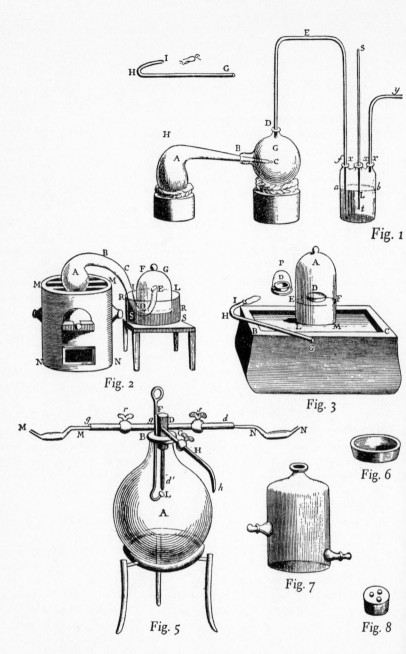

Lavoisier's apparatus, shown in his *Traité élémentaire de chimie*. The drawings were made by Mme. Lavoisier, who did nearly all the illustrations of his writings.

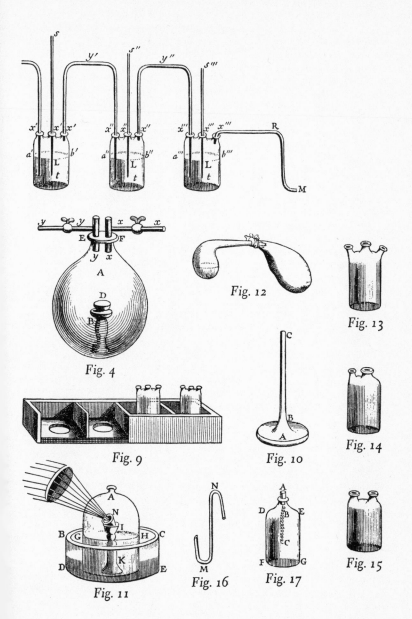

Fig. 12

Fig. 13

Fig. 4

Fig. 9

Fig. 10

Fig. 14

Fig. 11

Fig. 16

Fig. 17

Fig. 15

nothing but a combination of common air and phlogiston."
He was certain that it was not. He said:

> Since charcoal disappears completely in the revivifica-
> tion of the mercuric calx and since only mercury and fixed
> air are produced by this operation, one is forced to con-
> clude that the principle to which has hitherto been given
> the name of fixed air, is the result of the combination of
> the eminently respirable part of the air with charcoal; and
> this is what I propose to develop in a more satisfactory
> manner in subsequent memoirs which I shall devote to
> this object.

Thus, to the discerning eyes of history, he revealed his
debt to Priestley. He was never able, however, to acknowledge his debt fully and frankly. His nearest approach was
a rather grudging statement of 1776:

> Perhaps strictly speaking there is nothing in it [that is,
> the discovery of the new air] of which Mr. Priestley would
> not be able to claim the original idea; but since the same
> facts have conducted us to diametrically opposite results,
> I trust that if I am reproached for having borrowed my
> proofs from the works of this celebrated philosopher, my
> right to the conclusions will not be contested.

Later he reasserted his claim to independent discovery of
the new air. He spoke of it in 1782 as "this air which Mr.
Priestley discovered at very nearly the same time as I and
I believe even before me." He spoke of it in 1789 as "this
air, which was discovered nearly at the same time by Mr.
Priestley, Mr. Scheele and myself."

The Direct Attack on the Phlogiston Theory

One must be careful not to overemphasize Lavoisier's
debt to Priestley, out of irritation with him for failing
properly to acknowledge it at all. Francis Bacon, in a

famous passage of his *Novum Organum* (Book I, Apho-
rism xcv), wrote: "The men of experiment are like the
ant: they only collect and use; the reasoners resemble
spiders who make cobwebs out of their own substance. But
the bee takes a middle course; it gathers its material from
the flowers of the garden and the field, but transforms and
digests it by a power of its own." The metaphor, deprecat-
ing the ant while exalting the bee, may well be deplored
by any scientist who happens to be an entomologist, but
its intended meaning is clear. In Bacon's view the most
valuable contributions to human knowledge are made, not
by the hit-or-miss empiricist (the ant) or by the purely speculative reasoner (the spider), but by the true scientist (the
bee). The latter, having factual observations at hand, draws
logical inferences from them, and out of these inferences
he shapes general laws, whereby hitherto unrelated facts
are connected as elements of a single pattern.

Lavoisier was in perfect, if tacit, agreement with this.
The brilliant Frenchman regarded Priestley as an eminently useful "ant"; he regarded the ingeniously speculative phlogistonists as "spiders" that had ensnared chemistry, preventing its advance. He himself was the "bee"
who "transforms and digests" by a "power" of his own.
Nor was this view of his own role unjustified.

What Lavoisier learned from Priestley, after all, in regard to "dephlogisticated air," he would probably have
learned in a few months for himself by acting on the cues
provided by Bayen. He would certainly have learned it
from Scheele, with his "fire air," two or three years later.
Moreover, neither Priestley nor Scheele contributed ideas
to the grand conceptual scheme which Lavoisier was in
the process of creating. On the contrary, they opposed his
creation, both of them, for the Swede was as weak a theoretician as the Englishman and, like the Englishman, remained a phlogistonist until he died. To what extent, then,

was it true to say that Priestley or Scheele discovered oxygen? This was Lavoisier's question. Did they not refuse to recognize oxygen's actual function in chemical transformations? Their eyes may have seen it first—he was forced reluctantly to admit—but his were the first to recognize it for what it was.

Moreover, if Lavoisier lacked the kind of honesty that Priestley abundantly possessed, he had a kind of intellectual pride that is often the practical equivalent of scrupulosity. He failed in his efforts to acquire for himself historical credits belonging to others. This failure was not wholly the result of external factors; it resulted in part from the inner check imposed by his pride and enforced by his intelligence. He could not bring himself to acknowledge his scientific debts in full, nor, on the other hand, could be bring himself to deny them in full. He could not resist temptations to fake experimental evidence just a little bit now and then, in his eagerness to publish conclusions he knew *must* be true since they were logically implied by other firmly established truths; nor could he resist the felt need, rooted in his pride, to correct such falsifications. He redid his experiments until they were successful, and when they at last justified the conclusions he had prematurely published or when they required some modification of these, he revised and corrected his memoirs. In sum, his character defects seem minor when they are measured against the genius that ultimately triumphed over them.

Finally, care must be taken not to overstress Lavoisier's inferiority to Priestley and Scheele as an experimenter. He *was* their inferior in laboratory skill and ingenunity; few men in all chemical history have been their equal. But he was their superior in the devising of experiments (the setting up of models) that truly expressed and tested clearly conceived hypotheses.

In this respect nothing of Priestley's matches Lavoisier's

most famous experiment—a classic of laboratory science that he apparently performed for the first time in the spring of 1776 and reported for the first time, without details, in a memoir on the respiration of animals read to the Academy at a *rentrée publique* on May 3, 1777. A dozen years passed before he published a detailed description of it, with a drawing of the apparatus employed. The

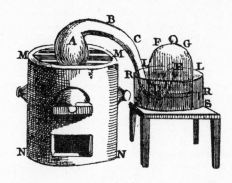

Lavoisier's apparatus for investigating the composition of air, from his *Traité élémentaire de chimie.*

description is worth quoting at length because of its importance in the development and ultimate acceptance of Lavoisier's new theory:

> I took a matrass A of capacity about 36 cubic inches with a very long neck BCDE of internal diameter about 6 to 7 lines [a line equaled one-twelfth of an inch]. I bent the neck as shown, in such a way that it could be placed on a furnace MMNN, while the extremity E of its neck could be inserted under the bell-jar FG, placed in a trough of mercury RRSS. I put four ounces of pure mercury into the matrass and then, by suction with a siphon which I introduced under the bell-jar FG, I raised the mercury to LL: I carefully marked this height with a strip of gummed paper and I noted accurately the readings of the barometer and thermometer.

The apparatus being thus prepared, I lighted a fire in the furnace MMNN, which I kept up almost continually for twelve days, in such a way that the mercury was heated nearly to the degree necessary to make it boil.

Nothing remarkable occurred during the first day: the mercury, though not boiling, was in a state of continual evaporation; it covered the inside of the vessels with small drops, which, at first very minute, afterwards increased in size and, when they had acquired a certain volume, fell back into the bottom of the vessel and were reunited with the rest of the mercury. On the second day, I began to see swimming on the surface of the mercury small red particles, which gradually increased in number and size during four or five days, after which they ceased to increase and remained completely unchanged. At the end of twelve days, seeing that the calcination of the mercury made no further progress, I extinguished the fire and allowed the vessels to cool. The volume of air contained in the matrass, in its neck and in the bell-jar [at a pressure and temperature which he gave], was about 50 cubic inches at the beginning of the experiment. When the experiment was completed, the volume of the air, reduced to the same pressure and temperature, was only about 42 to 43 cubic inches; a decrease in volume of about one-sixth had therefore occurred. On the other hand, having carefully collected the red particles that had formed and having separated them as much as possible from the liquid mercury with which they were mixed, I found that their weight was 45 grains. . . .

The air that remained after the experiment, and which had been reduced to five-sixths of its volume by the calcination of the mercury, was no longer fit either for respiration or for combustion; for animals that were put into it perished in a few seconds and candles were extinguished immediately, as if they had been plunged into water.

On the other hand, I took the 45 grains of red matter that had been formed during the experiment; I put them into a very small glass retort, to which was fitted an apparatus suitable for receiving the liquid or aeriform [having the form of air] products that might be separated: having lighted the fire in the furnace, I observed that, in proportion as the red matter grew hot, the intensity of its color increased. When the retort was almost glowing hot, the red matter began gradually to decrease in bulk and in a few minutes it disappeared completely; at the same time $41\frac{1}{2}$ grains of liquid mercury were condensed in the small receiver and 7 to 8 cubic inches of an elastic fluid, much fitter than the air of the atmosphere for supporting both combustion and the respiration of animals, passed over into the bell-jar.

A part of this air being put into a glass tube of about one inch in diameter, a candle was plunged into it and burned in it with a dazzling splendor; charcoal, instead of being consumed quietly as in ordinary air, burned in it with a flame and a kind of decrepitation, like phosphorus, and with a brilliancy of light that the eyes could hardly bear. . . . At first I gave . . . [this air] the name of *eminently respirable air* for which since has been substituted that of *vital air.*

The whole inquiry was a nearly perfect example of what Lavoisier came to insist should be the type of all experimental inquiry in chemistry. The quotation is from his masterwork, *Traité élémentaire de chimie* ("Treatise on the Elements of Chemistry"), the most important single book ever published in the field of chemistry, wherein he said:

Chemistry affords two general methods of determining the constituent principles of bodies, the method of analysis, and that of synthesis. When, for instance, by combining water with alcohol, we form the species of liquor called . . . spirit of wine, we certainly have the right to conclude, that . . . spirit of wine, is composed of alcohol combined with water. We can procure the same result by the analytical method [that is, by breaking the "spirit of wine" into its constituents of water and alcohol]; and in general it ought to be considered as a principle of chemical science, never to rest satisfied without both these species of proofs.

Both "species" were employed, as we have seen, in the mercury experiments. First the calx was "synthesized" of "vital air" and liquid mercury, then it was "analyzed" into liquid mercury and "vital air," and before and after each operation the materials were carefully weighed and measured.

Approximately a year after this experiment Lavoisier prepared a memoir contending that all acids were compounds of "vital air" (or "eminently respirable air") with nonmetallic substances—such as sulfur, phosphorus, and carbon—and that "vital air" was therefore the "acidifying principle" or, as it had better be called, "oxygen" (from the Greek *oxys,* meaning "sharp" or "acid," and the root of *gignesthai,* meaning "to be born"). He was mistaken in his conclusion: Oxygen is *not* an essential part of every acid, as he later learned, but the name he bestowed on it remains attached to the element.

Moreover, by the time he bestowed it, his theory of combustion had been completed. Combustion was a process of *oxidation;* its end product was an oxygen compound. In all cases the calcination of metals was, as he had shown it to be in the case of mercury, a union of metal with oxygen; reversed, it yielded oxygen and metal. Phlogiston was at best a needless complication. At worst (and he believed the worst of it), it was a snare and a delusion. He refrained from any direct attack on it, however, until a series of persuasive memoirs from his laboratory and study had undermined its foundations, forcing its defenders more and more onto the defensive. The elderly and highly respected Pierre Macquer, for instance, writing to his fellow scientist Guyton de Morveau, confessed dismay as he contemplated the consequences of Lavoisier's "surprising discovery" which seemed "to overthrow the phlogiston theory." He shrank from the prospect of having completely "to rebuild ... the old chemistry." [2] He preferred a compromise between the old theory and the new discovery and strove to make one in the 1778 edition of his *Dictionnaire de chimie* by asserting that phlogiston was the pure matter of light, rather than of heat (fire being both), and as such could penetrate the pores of vessels. Alas, this was no defense of the old theory at all, for it denied the "earthy element" which was of the essence of the Becher-Stahl doctrine. It was a new theory, Macquer's theory, and logical analysis in terms of the new facts proved it to be as wavering and self-contradictory as the old.

Lavoisier made this analysis as part of one of the greatest and most influential of all his memoirs, the *Réflexions sur le Phlogistique* ("Reflections on Phlogiston") of 1783, deemed by Douglas McKie to be "one of the most notable documents in the history of chemistry and of far greater historical significance than Boyle's *Sceptical Chymist*." [3] It was a slashing attack made with the intellectual weapon known to logicians as "Occam's razor"—a weapon that had been used with destructive effect on the medieval synthesis as the way was being prepared for the rise of Protestantism and science. The so-called "razor" is a maxim, attributed to an English schoolman, William of Occam (1300?-1350?): "Entities are not to be multiplied without necessity." Occam actually said: "It is vain to do with more what can be done with fewer." What he meant was that the simplest adequate solution is always preferable to the more complex; where everything can be explained without reference to some hypothetical entity, there is no basis for assuming that this entity exists. Phlogiston, argued Lavoisier, was just such an entity. All the known facts could be explained without it—and better explained.

Indeed, the effect of Stahl's doctrine (formulated before the main facts of combustion were known) was the very reverse of a reasonable process of explanation: It required a twisting of the observed facts into an alleged support of the theory which presumed to explain them. Again and again Lavoisier referred to the weight changes that occur during combustion and calcination. Again and again he revealed in its naked absurdity the circularity of the "reasoning" with which the phlogistonists sought to explain these changes. Always such "explanations" were purely verbal, purely *ad hoc;* they merely named what had happened, as if a label alone could be an effective cause of the thing labeled, and unlike his own theory, they had no predictive value whatever. On the contrary, every newly discovered fact seemed to require of the phlogistonists a radical revision of their doctrine. Thus, with Macquer's thesis that phlogiston was the "pure matter of light." Thus, with Guyton de Morveau's thesis that phlogiston had levity, or negative weight.

> [C]hemists have made phlogiston a vague principle which is not strictly defined and which consequently fits all the explanations required of it; [wrote Lavoisier] sometimes the principle has weight, sometimes it has not; sometimes it is free fire, sometimes it is fire combined with earth; sometimes it passes through the pores of vessels, sometimes these are impenetrable to it; it explains at once causticity and non-causticity, transparency and opacity, color and the absence of color. It is a veritable Proteus that changes its form every instant.
>
> [It was high time, he went on] to lead chemistry back to a stricter way of thinking, to strip the facts, with which this science is daily enriched, of the additions of rationality and prejudice, to distinguish what is fact and observation from what is system and hypothesis, and, in short, to mark out, as it were, the limit that chemical knowledge has reached so that those who come after it may set out from

that point and confidently go forward to the advancement of the science.

The memoir thus far was clearly a masterpiece of thought. It was incisive in its analysis, convincing in its ordering of information, and altogether devastating in its effect on the most famous (or infamous) *ad hoc* theory in the history of modern science. Yet at this point Lavoisier introduced some reasoning of his own that was almost as purely *ad hoc* and almost as purely circular as that which he just attacked! The irony is significant: Even great genius may fall prey to elementary logical fallacies as it proceeds beyond the frontiers of certain knowledge.

Lavoisier's experimental method and way of thinking about chemical phenomena owed much (how much has become a matter of controversy) to Joseph Black. Less fortunate was the use to which he put another borrowing from Black. In the early 1760's the great Scotsman was the first person to determine scientifically (by careful measurement) that equal applications of heat to equal quantities of different substances did *not* produce equal increases in the temperatures of the substances. (For instance, if you put equal weights of iron and water side by side atop a hot stove, you will find that the iron grows too hot to handle while the water is growing merely lukewarm.) Obviously some substances had a greater "capacity for heat" than others, and a distinction had to be made between "heat" and "temperature," although the two terms had been confused with each other ever since Galileo made the first crude thermometer. Temperature was a measurement of heat that was in some sort of combination with a substance. But what, then, was heat "in itself"? Black had what John Robison, the editor of his only (and posthumous) book, called "an almost morbid horror of generalization." He therefore declined to commit himself beyond the observed facts, save to admit that the "most probable idea" of it seemed to him to have been put forward by William Cleghorn in 1779. Cleghorn had described the "matter of heat" as a "subtle elastic fluid," whose "particles" had a "strong repulsion for one another" but were strongly attracted to the "particles" of "other kinds of matter." This, however, was "altogether a supposition," and to it, said Black, there was one strong objection— namely, that there was no experimental evidence "that the weight of bodies is increased by their being heated, or by the presence of heat in them." The "matter of heat," if it existed, must be "imponderable" (weightless). Certainly it was, in the prevailing state of knowledge, a purely hypothetical entity.

Now one would expect Lavoisier to reject this hypothesis categorically, since his whole system of chemistry depended on a precise balancing of weights. Instead, he accepted it! He did so, in the *Reflections,* a bit defensively: It was the only hypothetical entity involved in his theory, he said, and did nothing to weaken his position vis-à-vis the phlogistonists since they too recognized it. But he felt that he had somehow to account for the fact that combustion (oxidation) takes place only at certain definite temperatures, and he believed that the assumption of a "matter of heat" would enable him to do it. Experiments showed that oxygen (vital air) had a greater affinity for the "matter of heat" and therefore contained more of it than any other known air, he asserted. It was the mutual repulsiveness of the particles of heat that kept the particles of vital air apart —kept the oxygen, that is, in a state of elastic fluidity—and it was only by overcoming the affinity of the heat particles for the oxygen particles that the latter could come together to form solid compounds with metals. The latter event occurred, of course, because there was also an affinity between oxygen and metal. Thus, two attractive forces might be said to vie with each other for the allegiance of oxygen, and at a certain temperature point the affinity between oxygen and metal became "stronger" than that between oxygen and the "matter of heat." At this point combustion occurred: The metal and oxygen came together in a calx, and heat was released.

This was an "explanation" that explained nothing! It merely recast in a highly complicated form what was originally a simple statement of observed fact—namely, that combustion occurred at definite temperatures and was accompanied by a release of heat. In the process of complication it introduced an entity, the "matter of heat," for whose actual existence there was no evidence whatever; it was as vulnerable to "Occam's razor" as the phlogiston theory. Nevertheless, Lavoisier clung to this hypothetical "matter of heat" through the remainder of his life, naming it *caloric* and incorporating it as one of the few flaws, almost the only major flaw, in his "new chemistry."

Chemistry Becomes a Science

On the completion of this "new chemistry" he was now far advanced, and every new discovery in chemistry spurred his progress. Sometimes the discovery contradicted a major detail, creating momentary consternation, but always the edifice as a whole was enlarged by new blocks of solid information, held together by ever stronger bonds of logical consistency. This was notably true of the immensely important discovery of the composition of water.

In 1766, Henry Cavendish had discovered hydrogen, which he called "inflammable air" and thought of as pure phlogiston released from metal by the action on it of sulfuric or hydrochloric acid. In 1781 Priestley began to experiment with mixtures of "inflammable air" and "dephlogisticated air" in closed vessels through which an electric spark was passed. Not unexpectedly, he found that the spark triggered a violent explosion; as a matter of fact, he had, with a candle, exploded mixtures of these two airs as early as 1775, not long after he had first isolated "dephlogisticated air." (Of the earlier experiment he had written: "I easily conjectured, that inflammable air would explode with more violence, and a louder report, by the aid of dephlogisticated than of common air; but the effect far exceeded my expectations. . . .") Less expected was a reduction in the volume of the mingled airs which each such explosion effected. Not expected at all was the fact that a mist was formed on the walls of the confining vessel. Priestley noted the mist but made no scientific effort to explain it. He did, however, tell Cavendish of his inquiries, whereupon the latter repeated them with characteristic refinements, paying closer attention to weight and volume proportions than Priestley had done and testing with care the properties of the dew deposited by each explosion.

For this purpose Cavendish made use of a device known as a Volta eudiometer—a closely calibrated and graduated tube equipped with an electric sparking device. He found "that when inflammable air and common air are exploded in the proper proportion, almost all the inflammable air, and near one-fifth of the common air, lose their elasticity, and are condensed into dew . . . [and] that this dew is plain water, and consequently that almost all the inflammable air, and about one-fifth of the common air, are turned into water!" In other words, it appeared that water, the last of Empedocles' "four elements" to remain chemically unchallenged, was, like the other three (fire, earth, and air), not an element at all. Cavendish then conducted experiments with "inflammable" air and "dephlogisticated" air and found that when two volumes of the former were mixed with one of the latter, all of both airs was condensed into water and the weight of the water equaled the combined weights of the airs. He sought to explain this in terms of the phlogiston theory. Strictly speaking, water by this view was not a *compound* of the two airs but, instead, was released by the two, both of which had originally contained it. "Inflammable" air was phlogisticated water; "dephlogisticated" air was evidently dephlogisticated water —water that had been deprived of its phlogiston. The effect, however, was that water was a composed substance, susceptible to decomposition.

Cavendish, an investigator of almost incredible patience and exactness, refrained from publishing the results of these experiments until he had accounted for the puzzling fact that occasionally the water he obtained from the explosions was slightly acid. Very precise experiments were required to discover that the acidity occurred only when traces of what he called "mephitic" or "phlogisticated" air (nitrogen) were present in his apparatus. The acid proved to be what we now call nitric acid. All this required time, years in fact. It was not until January 15, 1784, in a paper read before the Royal Society, that Cavendish made formal announcement of his experiments.

Well before that time, however, word of what Cavendish was up to had got abroad and had produced a flurry of excited activity in other laboratories and studies. Priestley in late 1782 set out to "convert water into air" on the hypothesis that water was simply pure atmospheric air that had become saturated with phlogiston. Drive out the phlogiston and pure air would remain. He even announced in a letter to his friend James Watt (1736-1819), dated the day after Christmas, 1782, that "I now convert water into air— in the greatest quantity and with the least possible expense." The air, he went on, "is of the purity of that of the atmosphere." Watt, pondering this, reached the same conclusion as Cavendish had by then reached; namely, that water "is composed of dephlogisticated and inflammable air—and [that] dephlogisticated or pure air is composed of water deprived of phlogiston." Alas, Priestley in this case had blundered badly, as he ruefully admitted with characteristic frankness. He had used an earthenware retort, through whose pores water vapor had passed out and atmospheric air had pushed in. He converted no water to air when he used a glass retort.

Lavoisier, too, was directly stimulated by Cavendish's work into investigations of his own. In June, 1783, Cavendish's assistant, Charles Blagden, later secretary of the Royal Society, was in Paris, where he told Lavoisier of the results of Cavendish's 1781 experiments and of the "conclusion drawn from them" (Blagden's own later words). Lavoisier's reaction mingled astonishment with skepticism and gratification with dismay. That a liquid should prove to be the product of a combustion of inflammable air (for this was his interpretation of the result) was initially surprising, but he quickly saw that the process was perfectly in accord with his general theory. It was essentially the same process that converted a metal into a calx wherein vital air was "fixed." That the liquid should prove to be pure water, however, seemed to him at first incredible. In part this may have been because his mind had been long conditioned to regard fire and water as mutually antagonistic; it was hard to conceive of water as being "born," so to speak, of fire. But the major source of his astonishment, his skepticism, and his dismay was that the result flatly contradicted his specific theory (which had seemed to him abundantly proved by experiment) that vital air or oxygen is the "acidifying principle." The explosion of a mixture of hydrogen and oxygen *ought* to produce an acid.

It didn't, however. Lavoisier proved this to himself by repeating the Cavendish experiments hastily and rather clumsily in his own laboratory, with the assistance of Pierre

Simon de Laplace, famous as an astronomer and mathematician, and in the presence of Blagden and five other knowledgeable observers. This was on June 24. The next day Lavoisier submitted to the Academy a report that he and Laplace had "lately repeated in the presence of several members of the Academy the combustion of combustible with dephlogisticated air . . . [and that] the result was water in a very pure state." In November of the same year, he read to the Academy at a *rentrée publique* a memoir entitled *Mémoire où l'on prouve, par la décomposition de l'Eau, que ce Fluide n'est pas une substance simple. . . .* ("Memoir on Experiments to Prove, by the Decomposition of Water, that this Substance is not an Element, but can be decomposed and recombined"). In it he referred to some inconclusive experiments he had conducted with a colleague in 1777 to test the latter's opinion that the burning of "inflammable air" over limewater would yield "fixed air." He now said that the discoveries then made (none, in fact, had been made) had been "confirmed" by Cavendish, who had also noted, apparently in the process of the alleged "confirmation," that "a sensible amount of moisture was produced." The memoir continued: "As the verification of this fact was of extreme importance for chemical theory, M. Lavoisier and M. de la Place [sic] proposed to verify it by an experiment on a large scale. . . ." Blagden, the memoir continued, was present at this experiment, he having *"informed us* that Mr. Cavendish had already tried, in London, to burn inflammable air in closed vessels, and that *he had obtained a very sensible quantity of water."* There followed a description of the experiment and of a subsequent one, highly unsatisfactory, wherein iron filings with a little water were placed in a bell jar of atmospheric air inverted over mercury. As the iron rusted, "inflammable air" was released and "dephlogisticated air" was absorbed into the iron rust, thus "proving" that water had been decomposed into the two airs.

The memoir was promptly published (December, 1783), in Rozier's *Journal,* a month before Cavendish made his first public report of his experiments. It sparked the same kind of acrimonious controversy that had swirled around Lavoisier following the "Easter Memoir" and for the same reason. It was obvious to the indignant Blagden that Lavoisier was trying to claim far more credit than he deserved. In a letter published in another scientific periodical, Blagden wrote:

> In general, Mr. Lavoisier cannot be convicted of having advanced anything contrary to truth, but it can be still less denied that he concealed part of the truth; for he should have acknowledged that I had, some days before, apprised him of Mr. Cavendish's experiments, instead of which the expression *"the latter informed us"* gives rise to the idea that I had not informed him earlier than that very day. In like manner, Mr. Lavoisier has passed over a very remarkable circumstance—namely, that the experiment was made in consequence of what I had informed him. He should likewise have stated in his publication not only that Mr. Cavendish had obtained *"a very sensible quantity of water"* but that the water was equal to the weight of the two airs added together. . . .

This controversy was also similar to the one with Priestley insofar as Lavoisier—although he was not the first person to observe the facts—might justly claim to be the first person to understand them, the first to fit them into a general theory whereby the composition of water was shown to be consistent with the composition of other chemical compounds and with the chemical reactions by which these were formed. The whole episode, wrote one of Lavoisier's biographers, Marcelin Berthelot, "is an incident in the long-standing feud, continually being renewed in the history of science, *between the sagacious discoverers of particular facts and the men of genius who frame general theories."* [4] Insofar as it had any effect at all on scientific progress, it was slightly to impede the progress of Lavoisier's "revolution" in chemistry by raising barriers of personal animosity between him and the scientists who might otherwise have accepted his general theory.

The "revolution" nevertheless progressed. In the early 1780's, acting on the original suggestion of Guyton de Morveau, Lavoisier worked with Guyton de Morveau, Antoine François Fourcroy, and Claude Louis Berthollet in the development of a consistent system of chemical nomenclature. One was badly needed and long overdue. The first fruits of these labors were presented in a memoir read before a *rentrée publique* of the Academy on April 18, 1787, by Lavoisier, the acknowledged leader of the four. His task was to present the philosophy, the general principles that had guided them. The actual nomenclature and details of the system were to be presented later by Guyton de Morveau.

Lavoisier began with a reference to a statement by the Abbé Etienne Bonnot de Condillac to the effect that languages are "analytical methods" which are essential to the art of reasoning since the art of reasoning is that of analyzing. But a language is not only this, but also "a collection of representative signs." This fact, said Lavoisier, presented "observations of another kind." He continued:

In this second point of view, we shall have three objects to consider in every physical science, namely, the series of facts that constitute the science, the ideas that recall the facts, and the words that express them. The word should give birth to the idea and the idea should portray the fact: these are three impressions of the same seal. And, since it is the words that preserve the ideas and transmit them, it follows that it is impossible to improve the science without perfecting the language and that, however correct the ideas they refer to, they will still transmit only false impressions if we have no exact expressions to convey them. The perfection of chemical nomenclature, considered in this respect, consists in rendering the ideas and facts in their exact truth, without suppressing anything they present and above all without adding anything to them: it must be nothing but a faithful mirror; for, we cannot repeat it too often, it is neither Nature nor the facts she presents, but our own reason that deceives us.

What Lavoisier was insisting on here was a neutral vocabulary, a language as rigorously objective as mathematics.

He went on to restate the definition of "element" that Boyle had made in *The Sceptical Chymist*—namely, that "an element is a substance that cannot be decomposed into other substances." The "cannot," however, should be regarded as tentative, deriving from the present state of chemical knowledge and subject to removal as this knowledge grew. Many substances that now appeared to be simple elements would doubtless prove in the future to be compounds, "and we are probably approaching this epoch with regard to siliceous earth and the fixed alkalis."

Two weeks later, on May 2, 1787, Guyton de Morveau read to the Academy the memoir that presented in detail the nomenclature and system of classification. *Gas* replaced "air," *hydrogen* replaced "inflammable air," and *azote* (*a* for "no" and *zote* for "life") became the name of "phlogisticated air" or, as we now call it, nitrogen. *Oxygen,* previously coined, was retained as the name of "dephlogisticated air." The "pure principle of charcoal" was named *carbon,* "fixed air" was named *carbonic acid;* and the salts formed by this acid became *carbonates.* The terms *sulfates, phosphates,* and *nitrates* were introduced. The two acids of sulfur became *sulfuric* and *sulfurous;* those of nitrogen became *nitric* and *nitrous* acids. Metallic calxes became metallic *oxides*—iron *oxide*, lead *oxide*, etc. But there is here no need to summarize further this historic memoir. On page 177 is a facsimile of the table Fourcroy drew up, showing in parallel columns the classification system, the new names of substances, and the old names.

Nor is there need to recount in any detail the resistance made to the new language by those who had grown up with the old and were emotionally committed to it. Suffice it to say that the Academy's committee appointed to review the work damned it with very faint praise indeed, while others damned its authors for "high treason against our ancestors" (the quotation is from Thomas Thomson), sacrilege, and desecration. Even the great Black was bitterly opposed, reacting as if he had been personally offended by what he sarcastically referred to as the "junto of French chemists." As for Black's student and editor, John Robison, he was convinced that a "determination to be the founder of a system and a sect of philosophers" had "seduced Mr. Lavoisier and made him acquiesce in measures that may be called violent and unbecoming." Such attacks should have been expected, but their vehemence seems to have surprised and nettled Lavoisier. They were, of course, ineffective in the long run. The new nomenclature, based firmly and solely on Lavoisier's general theory, gained adherents at an accelerating rate during the immediately following years, and (remarkable fact) it is substantially the language of chemistry today.

It was as a continuation of this linguistic effort that Lavoisier shaped, half-inadvertently, his crowning masterpiece, the *Traité élémentaire de chimie* ("Treatise on the Elements of Chemistry"), published in Paris in 1789—a work that "laid the foundation of modern chemistry as securely as Newton's *Principia* had a century earlier laid the foundations of modern mechanics," to quote Douglas

McKie [5] Lavoisier confessed in his Preface to this book that at the outset he had had no intention of developing a systematic treatise on chemistry. Instead, his purpose had been to expand and explain further his 1787 memoir on the new nomenclature. His soon discovered, however, that this purpose was actually identical with that of the treatise he now presented, since the nomenclature of chemistry and the science itself were inextricably mingled and even fused. Referring to the crucial importance to science of correcting "reason" by experiments, he said he had "imposed" on himself "the law of never advancing but from the known to the unknown, or deducing no consequence that does not immediately derive from experiments and observations."

Here again there is no need to review Lavoisier's work in any detail. With its publication the "revolution" in chemistry which he had envisaged sixteen years before was completed, for its impact was immediate and (with a few stubborn, elderly exceptions) overwhelming.

The treatise listed thirty-three elements, including *caloric* for "heat" and *lumière* for "light." It explicated his oxygen theory and described the general processes of chemical combination and decomposition, including the formation of metallic salts, in terms that are still accepted as true. It presented the fact that substances may exist in three states—solid, liquid, and gaseous—and theorized that these depend on the amount of imponderable caloric with which the ponderable substances are combined and interpenetrated. Most important of all, it enunciated for the first time with clarity and precision what is known as the "law" of the conservation of mass—a conception that seems a natural outgrowth of Lavoisier's bourgeois background and experience since it applies to chemical phenomena the principle of the balance sheet and makes possible the presentation of chemical reactions as equations. What the

	Noms nouveaux.	Noms anciens correspondans.
	Lumière.........	Lumière.
Subftances fimples qui appartiennent aux trois règnes & qu'on peut regarder comme les élémens des corps.	Calorique........	Chaleur.
		Principe de la chaleur.
		Fluide igné.
		Feu.
		Matière du feu & de la chaleur.
	Oxygène.........	Air déphlogiftiqué.
		Air empiréal.
		Air vital.
		Bafe de l'air vital.
	Azote...........	Gaz phlogiftiqué.
		Mofète.
		Bafe de la mofète.
	Hydrogène.......	Gaz inflammable.
		Bafe du gaz inflammable.
Subftances fimples non métalliques oxidables & acidifiables.	Soufre...........	Soufre.
	Phofphore........	Phofphore.
	Carbone.........	Charbon pur.
	Radical muriatique.	Inconnu.
	Radical fluorique .	Inconnu.
	Radical boracique.	Inconnu.
Subftances fimples métalliques oxidables & acidifiables.	Antimoine........	Antimoine.
	Argent..........	Argent.
	Arfenic..........	Arfenic.
	Bifmuth.........	Bifmuth.
	Cobolt..........	Cobolt.
	Cuivre..........	Cuivre.
	Etain...........	Etain.
	Fer............	Fer.
	Manganèfe.......	Manganèfe.
	Mercure.........	Mercure.
	Molybdène.......	Molybdène.
	Nickel..........	Nickel.
	Or............	Or.
	Platine.........	Platine.
	Plomb..........	Plomb.
	Tungftène.......	Tungftene.
	Zinc...........	Zinc.
Subftances fimples falifiables terreufes.	Chaux..........	Terre calcaire, chaux.
	Magnéfie........	Magnéfie, bafe du fel d'Epfom.
	Baryte..........	Barote, terre pefante.
	Alumine........	Argile, terre de l'alun, bafe de l'alun.
	Silice..........	Terre filiceufe, terre vitrifiable.

Lavoisier's table of the elements, from his *Traité élémentaire de chimie.*

"law" says is that although the forms of things may be drastically changed by the application of heat and by other actions on them, the total mass is neither diminished nor increased. Matter per se is "indestructible." The truth of this "law" had been implicitly assumed by Lavoisier at the very outset of his career as a chemist in his experiments to determine whether or not water was transmutable into earth by means of heat.

Of course, every schoolboy knows that the "law" has had to be modified in the present century. Modern physics has demonstrated that whenever energy (heat) is released or absorbed in chemical changes, there must be a decrease or increase of mass in accordance with Einstein's famous equation $E = mc^2$. In the case of nuclear fission or fusion the transformation of mass into energy is drastic. But for all ordinary changes this decrease or increase is far too slight to be detectable. The mass conservation law continues to hold for all practical purposes, and to Lavoisier belongs the major credit for establishing it as basic to experimental chemistry.

5. Lavoisier and the French Revolution

Turgot Gives the Old Regime Its Last Chance

On May 9, 1774, about five months before Joseph Priestley made his first and only visit to Paris, Louis XV died in the vast and glittering palace built by his predecessor, the Sun King, at Versailles. He is supposed to have muttered on his deathbed, *"Après moi, le déluge* ['After me, the deluge'],"* but this is probably apocryphal. What is certain is that he died of smallpox, that the stench surrounding his deathbed was nauseating, and that the unmitigated nastiness of his demise seemed to his subjects to be perfectly consistent with the nature of his reign. He was dead only a few moments when his already putrefying corpse was dumped without ceremony into a coffin and hurried from the palace to the royal cemetery at St. Denis. It was night. Few people were in the streets to witness the passage of the royal bier. Those few jeered.

No genius was required to see a solution, in the abstract, to the most pressing problems that had faced the Sun King's

179

successor as, after some years of regency rule, he assumed the royal power. Common sense sufficed: Privilege must be severely reduced, the extravagances of the nobility must be curtailed, and its members must be forced to pay a substantial portion of the taxes which then crushed the people least able to pay them. What was simple in the abstract, however, was exceedingly difficult in terms of concrete political realities. The latter imposed on the monarch a necessity for greatness of character, joined to leadership qualities of a high order. Alas, the only great thing about Louis XV was his sexual appetite. This was enormous and wholly beyond the control of his flabby mind and will. As a result, his successive mistresses—notably Mme. de Pompadour and Mme. du Barry—had a large part in the management or mismanagement of affairs of state. The country was near bankruptcy. Wrath and hatred filled the widening breach between the people and the privileged orders. Only the most drastic reforms could prevent a violent social upheaval—given the prevailing context of science, philosophy, and trade.

For a brief time it appeared that these reforms would be made. Great hopes attended the elevation to the throne of the new king, Louis XVI, who was then twenty years old. None who had known him as dauphin thought him brilliant of intellect, but many had found him amiable and well intentioned, free of vice (remarkably so, in view of his surroundings), and sincere in his wish to repair the damage done the state during the last years of his predecessor's reign. His first acts stirred a wave of popular enthusiasm. He refused to impose the heavy accession tax which normally accompanied a coronation, promised other tax remissions, and took steps toward a reduction in court expenses. He banished Mme. du Barry from the court and dismissed the Abbé Terray (Mme. Lavoisier's great-uncle) from the post of Controller General of Finance. (It is a measure of the popular esteem in which the Abbé was held that his carriage was attacked by a mob of hundreds when it appeared on the streets of Paris following his dismissal; he narrowly escaped being thrown, with his carriage, into the Seine.) Best of all, as an indication of the seriousness of his reforming zeal, was the king's replacement of the hated Abbé with the Physiocrat Anne Robert Jacques Turgot [1] whose accession to power seemed to his friend Voltaire to mark the beginning of "a new heaven and a new earth." Myriads shared these great expectations.

Turgot, sharing them, did his best to fulfill them. His mind was permeated with the doctrines of "natural right" and "natural law"; he therefore knew precisely what should be done and how to do it. His commitment to the general welfare was complete; he therefore expected such a commitment from those who initially promised him support. He had, in brief, the typical doctrinaire's impatience with those who could not see what to him was perfectly obvious or who, seeing it, nevertheless continued to act in the service of private selfish interests. Moreover, although his intimates knew him as a charming and witty man, warm in his personal affections and kindly in his general outlook, he was shy of strangers and generally impressed them as harsh of manner, cold of temperament, and arrogant of intellect. He had no talent for compromise. This was unfortunate for him, since it contributed to his downfall; it was tragic for France, insofar as it contributed to the failure of his reforms—although one may well doubt that any man, however blessed with the arts of persuasion, could have overcome the selfishness and political stupidity which characterized in general the French aristocracy and high clergy.

Upon his appointment in late August, 1774, Turgot told the young king that his policy would be "no bankruptcy, no increase in taxation, no borrowing"—a bold policy in the circumstances, but clearly necessary. The king agreed to it. If the king failed it at the very first test, when Turgot tried in vain to reduce the extravagant costs of the formal coronation ceremonies, he sustained his new minister in other matters. Turgot scored initial successes, even triumphs. Within three weeks after assuming his office, he had put into effect an edict requiring free trade in corn (wheat) within the country, despite the bitter opposition of many people in high places who had a speculative interest in grain. Within a few months he had restricted the profits of the *ferme générale* by establishing new terms for the renewal of farmer-general leases. Within half a year he had saved millions of livres by persuading the new king to limit pensions and grants to the privileged. By the end of 1775 he had managed to accumulate a surplus income over expenditures for the year of some 5,000,000 livres, compared with a deficit for 1774 of 48,600,000.

He pushed on. In the first month of the new year, 1776, a year in which the example of American Revolution fed the passion for popular liberty everywhere, he proposed to the king's council what became known to history as his "Six Edicts." One of these abolished the *corvée,* whereby peasants might at any time be drafted for forced labor on the highways, although their crops would rot unharvested in the fields. Another suppressed the trade guilds, whose privileges had prevented the liberty of commerce and industry which was a first principle of the Physiocratic creed. He longed to put into effect the prime article of this creed —namely, that all indirect taxes would be abolished in favor of a single direct tax on land—but was forced reluctantly to conclude that the national debt continued to be much too large to permit so drastic an experiment. Indeed, despite his announced policy of "no borrowing," he had at this time to negotiate a sizable loan to his government from some Dutch bankers, managing, however, to obtain

it at the unprecedentedly low interest rate of 4 percent—
a tribute to the success of his financial reforms.

As for his "Six Edicts," they were angrily opposed by
the privileged. The Parlement of Paris, refusing to register
them, exemplified the manner in which arguments of
"natural law" may be, and generally have been, used by
conservatives and reactionaries. "The first rule of justice
is to conserve for each individual that which belongs to
him," read the official declaration. "This is a fundamental rule of natural law . . . ; a rule which consists not only
in maintaining the rights of property but also those . . .
derived from prerogatives of birth and social position. . . .
To make the nobles subject to imposts levied in compen-
sation for abolishing the *corvée* . . . would be equivalent to
declaring the nobles subject to the *corvée* as well as the
laboring classes." A prominent number of members of the
Parlement stated flatly, as if it were integral to the natural
order, that "all public financial burdens *should* be borne
by the lower orders" since the nobles "are exempted by
birth from the imposition of all taxation." Nevertheless,
Turgot managed at last to obtain the registration of his
decrees through a *lit de justice* on March 12. It was a
Pyrrhic victory.

For there were now united against him the nobility
(they shuddered at the prospect of losing *all* their special
privileges); the clergy (they feared a loss of church power
to Protestantism, should complete religious freedom be
permitted); the financiers (they profited hugely from the
antiquated methods of borrowing and tax collecting which
Turgot proposed to abolish); most of the wealthiest of the
Paris bourgeoisie (they found themselves engaged in wage
disputes with their workers following the elimination of
the trade guilds); the military (Turgot, on grounds of
economy, opposed their desire for war against England
while the latter was occupied with the American revolt);

and the queen (vain, frivolous, foolish Marie Antoinette was infuriated by the minister's opposition to her granting of costly favors to her protégés). As for the young king, although increasingly stout of body, he proved a slender reed on which to lean as Turgot had to lean. His vague goodwill, inadequately sustained by strength of mind or character, was no match for the pressures imposed by those who knew exactly what they wanted. He was especially overmatched by his willful beautiful young queen, whom he loved. In late April 1776, he began to give way, and in May he gave way altogether. On May 12 he dismissed Turgot from office.

Great was the rejoicing in the queen's circle, although she would have been happier had Turgot been sent, as she tried to have him sent, to the Bastille. The king's brother, the Comte d'Artois, cried happily, "At last we shall have some money to spend!" Several bishops ordered that special prayers of thanksgiving be said in the churches.

But Voltaire mourned: "It is a disaster. I see nothing before me now but death. I am struck to the heart by this blow, and shall never be consoled for having seen the beginning and the end of the golden age that Turgot was preparing for us." Whether or not it was a "golden age," it was certainly ended, and with it ended the last clear chance of the Old Regime to transform itself peaceably, through a moderate transition, into a modern society.

Virtually all of Turgot's fundamental reforms were revoked within five months. Within ten years, during which five men in succession occupied the office of Controller General, a total national debt of 1,680,000,000 livres was accumulated, no new loans could be negotiated, and it was found to be impossible to impose new taxes on people whose tax burdens were already heavier than they could bear. The incumbent Controller General, Charles de Calonne, in a complete reversal of his policy, was forced to propose a drastic renovation of the tax structure and of local governmental administration. He tried desperately to persuade a hastily summoned "Convocation of Notables" to accept this in early 1787—and failed. The French aristocrats were blindly, stubbornly determined to maintain their privileges intact; they vehemently refused to bear a share of the nation's financial burdens.

So a whirlwind began to rise and turn over France. At its center was the great question: Who shall have the supreme governing power over the nation? Shall it be the king as an absolute monarch, on the lines established by Louis XIV? Shall it be the feudal nobility, as it was before the Great Louis consolidated national power in the throne and as it began to be again (although it had not yet become) under the weak Louis XV and Louis XVI? Or shall it be the sovereign people, the commons, as exemplified to a large degree in England's constitutional monarchy and to a greater degree in the emerging republic of the United States?

Lavoisier and the Politics of Reform

This was the politico-historical background for Lavoisier's great work as a chemist. It was far more than mere background, however, for others of Lavoisier's activities and for his life as a whole. He was by no means exclusively a chemist. He was also a businessman, a public administrator, an economic and social planner, a progressive agriculturist, and even an educational theorist—in short, a man of many public affairs. As such, he was directly involved in the political and social upheaval which began during Turgot's ministry and, after many vicissitudes, culminated in bloody revolution some fourteen years later. He was no leading figure in it. Most histories of the French Revolution do not mention his name; Carlyle's classic account

mentions only his death. Yet his part was by no means un-
important, and unlike that of many other leading figures,
it was genuinely creative. Almost everything that Lavoisier did as a direct consequence of the impact of politics on
him had a permanent value. He was eminently useful.

In the Paulze salon before his marriage, Lavoisier's associates were reformers of the Physiocratic school, among
them Turgot. Lavoisier continued his association with
such men after his marriage; he adopted in general their
theories of political economy. He favored, theoretically,
a single tax on land, freedom of trade and industry, and
the abolition of at least such portions of special privilege
as those preventing the nation from being governed by
those naturally best fitted for the task. But such reforming
zeal as he had came more from his head than from his
heart. His moral feelings may or may not have been deeply
outraged on occasion by the Old Regime; but his sense of
efficiency was certainly constantly outraged by it, and
although there is no evidence that he was normally moved
by great humanitarian passions, the evidence is abundant
that his life was ruled by an intellectual concept of order,
of balance, of consistent pattern. Others wished to change
the status quo because it was cruelly unjust; he wished to
change it because it was impractical.

Yet even if the great political issue of the day is exclusively defined in terms of efficiency versus inefficiency or
of rational economy versus extravagant privilege, Lavoisier's public position was inevitably ambivalent and ambiguous. He had a foot in each camp; he attempted to
make the best of two mutually antagonistic worlds.

As an academician, he performed a multitude of services
to the government and general public that aimed toward
an increase of efficiency and a decrease of waste. One has
only to glance over a list of the subjects of the reports he
made, either as the sole author or in collaboration with

others, to be impressed by the great number and range of these services. He reported on the methods of working coal mines, on the sanitary conditions of prisons and hospitals, on a new barrel design, on the manufacture of starch, on cesspool design and the "airs" emitted by cesspools, on sugar manufacture, on the construction of flour mills, on the distillation of saltwater to obtain drinking water on ships at sea, on fire-extinguishing liquids, on the methods of detecting counterfeit currency, on plate-glass manufacture, on the conversion of peat into charcoal, and on scores of other similarly practical matters. He officially observed and reported on the hot-air balloon invented by the Montgolfier brothers, which carried men aloft in free flight for the first time in October, 1783, and on the use of hydrogen in balloons. He served in 1781 on a special committee appointed to investigate scientifically the "animal magnetism" of Dr. Franz Anton Mesmer, for which extravagant claims of medical cures were being made—an investigation whose conclusion was that "animal magnetism" as defined by Mesmer did not exist. (One of the others on this committee was Dr. Joseph Ignace Guillotin, with whose instrument of humane execution Lavoisier was destined to become intimately familiar. Another was the American minister, Benjamin Franklin, appointed as an authority on electricity.) He served on numerous other special commissions and committees and was generally their most effective member.

At the same time he was a member of the *ferme générale*. From all accounts he was thoroughly honest in his *ferme* operations, suggesting and helping to put into effect numerous reforms, which not only increased the profit-making efficiency of the company but also reduced its evils as a collector of unjust taxes. For instance, he abolished a special tax that had been imposed on Jews in one district simply because they were Jews, and he reduced the amount of water added to the tobacco the *ferme* handled, saying to his colleagues that it "is better to be conservative in the soaking, to make lighter profits than to dissatisfy the people." Nevertheless, he personally profited—and richly—from this institution of privilege and exploitation, this active opponent of every proposed financial reform.

The unhappy ambiguity of his position was sharply exposed in the light of Turgot's attempted reforms. No organized group opposed these reforms more consistently, more bitterly than did the tax farmers, whose profits Turgot moved to reduce, and this opposition was an important factor in the minister's dismissal and in the wiping out of his major work. Where, then, stood Lavoisier, who was at one and the same time a Physiocrat and a farmer-general? Did he attempt to moderate or prevent the reactionary tactics of his colleagues in the *ferme?* There is no certain record that he did. Nor is there any clear record that he personally supported Turgot when the latter was in his greatest difficulties. All that is certain about the relationship between the two men during Turgot's ministry is that Turgot appointed Lavoisier to a position of trust, and there is significant irony in the fact that this appointment resulted in virtually the only important permanent reform achieved by the abortive "golden age."

When Turgot took office, the government relied for its supply of gunpowder, as it did for its supply of tax money, on a private company of financiers. A so-called *ferme des poudres* ("powder farm") contracted to supply a stated amount annually. The arrangement greatly profited the financiers at the expense of the government (they made an annual profit of about 30 percent on their invested capital), while it placed the national security in jeopardy during times of emergency. If less than the promised amount was delivered in any one year, the company was not required to make up the deficit during the year following; if more than the promised amount was needed in any one year, the company could not be required to supply it. The extra need must then be supplied from abroad at exorbitant prices.

The price of the home supply was high enough and was steadily increasing; its quality was low and steadily decreasing; for there was no incentive to improve either quantity or quality. On the contrary, the methods by which saltpeter was obtained were such as to reward the inefficient and dishonest. Saltpeter or niter (potassium nitrate, KNO_3) is formed in the soil of stables, barnyards, pigsties, dovecots, and privies—soil impregnated with animal excreta. By digging up this soil, the *salpêtriers,* as they were called, obtained the raw material (the ore, so to speak) of this essential ingredient, and they were granted the rights of free transportation from place to place, free lodgings at the expense of the villages, and free access to all private property where saltpeter might be found, property which might then be searched and dug up at their pleasure. Small wonder that the approach of these malodorous creatures was watched with sullen hostility and even with dread by peasants and villagers. Small wonder, too, that the *salpêtriers,* having in their hands so potent a power to annoy and injure, should often be offered and often accept bribes to exercise their power elsewhere, with a resultant decrease in the national supply of niter. As for the methods and proportions of the mixture of niter, charcoal, and sulfur to obtain explosive powder, they were almost as antiquated and inefficient as those of the niter gatherers.

All this Turgot proposed to change. He turned, naturally enough, to Lavoisier, who was both a brilliant chemist and an eminently practical businessman, and Lavoisier prepared a report on the powder farm, which was also a plan for its abolition and replacement. The report was accepted; the plan, adopted. A decree in early 1775 ordered the liquidation of the old *ferme* and the establishment in its place of a government corporation, known as the *régie des poudres* ("powder commission"), wherein the motives of individual private profit and collective public service were neatly welded. The *régie,* like the former *ferme,* was granted a complete monopoly of the manufacture and sale of powder, including that used for industrial and sporting purposes and that of low grade which was sold abroad, but unlike the old *ferme,* the new organization was not privately controlled. The four powder commissioners who headed it were state officials with a salary fixed at 2,400 livres annually. They could be removed from office by the government. Their salary, however, was intended to be merely a guaranteed base pay. The commissioners were to receive additional cash allowances as a stated percentage of the total sales of niter and powder. Thus, Lavoisier, whom Turgot appointed as one of the four and who became in effect the executive director of the whole enterprise, was soon receiving from this source an annual income of between 14,000 and 17,000 livres.

He was worth every bit of it. Under his direction the powder commission became a modern government bureau, staffed with civil servants who, as applicants, had been required to pass civil service examinations. Their pay was regularized, generally raised, and scaled in such a way as to provide incentives for good work. The oppressive and exploitive operations of the *salpêtriers* were moderated, when they were not abolished: The villages were no longer required to provide free transportation and lodgings for them or cartage for their dug-up earth, and the right to search and dig was severely restricted. Moreover, being better paid, the *salpêtriers* became better workmen. A review of all existing literature on the "formation and fabrication" of saltpeter was published in 1776 (the French title was *Receuil de Mémoires et d'Observations sur la forma-*

tion et sur la fabrication du Saltpêtre) for distribution to the subcommissions throughout France, and in the following year Lavoisier himself prepared a manual of instructions on the establishment of artificial niter beds and on the best methods of extracting saltpeter from them, in order to remove the ancient dependence on random searchings and diggings. He persuaded Turgot to order the Academy of Science to offer a substantial prize, to be awarded in 1778, for the best essay on the methods of preparing saltpeter, along with a review of the available information on the subject and suggestions for experiments which might be conducted. When none of the essays submitted was deemed worthy of the prize, the contest was renewed, and a prize of 8,000 livres was awarded in 1782. All the worthy essays submitted were then collected, edited, and published with an historical introduction. Simultaneously, Lavoisier studied the occurrence of saltpeter in chalk deposits, to which his attention had been called by his friend the Duc de la Rochefoucauld, and suggested possible methods of extracting it.

Most important, Lavoisier also applied his chemical genius to the improvement of the quality of the gunpowder manufactured, varying the proportions of the mixture of ingredients and sometimes trying new ingredients, in order to increase its explosive power. On one occasion his efforts in this direction became very nearly the cause of his death. This was in the autumn of 1788, shortly after his fellow scientist and academician Claude Louis Berthollet had discovered potassium chlorate ($KClO_3$) and had found that a mixture of this unstable compound with sulfur and charcoal was highly explosive. Lavoisier at once became interested in the possibility of using it instead of saltpeter in the manufacture of gunpowder—it was much more easily available than niter—and directed the superintendent of the powder factory at Essones, a man named Le Tort, to prepare a mixture. He also ordered the superintendent to protect the workmen by erecting a thick plank wall between them and the mixing vats. He himself traveled to Essones to watch the mixing, accompanied by Berthollet, Mme. Lavoisier, and M. and Mlle. Chevraud. Le Tort was careless or ignorant of the extreme danger involved in the mixing procedure. He led the party too near the vats on their unwalled side, and before Lavoisier's sharp warning protest could be heeded, there was a violent explosion. Le Tort and Mlle. Chevraud, who were in the forefront, were hurled against a wall of the factory behind them and killed. Lavoisier and the other three of the party were also thrown against the wall and were badly bruised, but were otherwise uninjured. None of the workmen, protected by the plank barricade, was hurt at all.

By that year, 1788, it was estimated that the *régie des poudres,* while making very substantial profits for itself, had saved the government approximately 28,000,000 livres. The annual output of powder had been increased from 1,600,000 pounds in 1775 to 3,777,000. The government magazines contained no less than 5,000,000 pounds of powder; moreover, this was now the best in the world, for the range of musket fire had been increased from between 136 and 155 meters in 1775 to between 244 and 255 meters by 1788. The range of artillery had been increased by a similar proportion, a factor of perhaps crucial importance to the French Revolution in 1792 and after, when the invading armies of neighboring monarchies attempted to crush it. The French might well have lost the decisive cannonade at Valmy if Charles François Dumouriez' artillery had been forced to use the inferior powder of 1775. One may also wonder if Napoleon could have won victory after victory through an unprecedented use of firepower had he not had at hand the abundance of superior gunpowder which existed mostly because of Lavoisier's work in the *régie des poudres.*

Another public service of Lavoisier's, consequent to Turgot's tenure of power, was that of governor (one of a board of governors) of the Discount Bank which Turgot had established to increase the availability of credit to commercial enterprises. It was a service which was marred by unethical conduct in 1783, during the brief ministry of Le Fèvre d'Ormesson, according to some hostile commentators, although the evidence is far from clear. All that is certain is that Le Fèvre d'Ormesson, desperate for cash with which to pay for the court extravagance that he failed as Controller General to curb, resorted to secret and illegal borrowings from the Discount Bank, which was soon forced to suspend payments; that Lavoisier, who must have known of the transactions, made no audible protest against them, as he would appear to have been duty-bound to do; and that simultaneously Le Fèvre d'Ormesson announced his "intention to have ... [Lavoisier] made a member of the Committee of Administration" of the *ferme générale.* The appearance is that of bribery, with Le Fèvre d'Ormesson paying off with a lucrative and prestigious post for Lavoisier's silence. But it is an appearance which may be wholly false, especially since there is some doubt whether Lavoisier actually received the appointment or, if he did, whether he ever actually served on the committee.

As the effective head of the powder commission, Lavoisier made his home in comfortable and spacious living quarters provided to him in the Arsenal of Paris, where he moved with Marie, his furniture, and all his fine laboratory equipment one day in the early spring of 1775. The chemical laboratory he then established in a large room of the Arsenal became probably the best equipped in all Europe. He spared no expense; he made full use of his growing wealth to secure the finest available apparatus. His precision balances, for instance, made by Jean Fortin, cost 600 livres apiece; his "apparatus for aerial experiments" (to use the phrase of an English visitor) cost about 50,000 livres! He who was often deemed avaricious and coldly acquisitive in his general attitudes was lavishly generous in his devotion to science. He was pleased to have young scientists of proved ability work with his equipment, under his general supervision, and he often opened his purse to those who were impoverished. Thus, the Arsenal laboratory, where he regularly spent six hours of each crowded day, became at once a kind of research institute, a mecca for visiting scientists from all over Europe, and in effect a part of the Lavoisier salon, where there gathered at one time or other virtually all the intellectual and many of the political leaders of France.

In 1784 he gave practical effect to Physiocratic doctrine by launching a remarkable economic study, which, although continued for seven years, was destined to be published without having been completed. Its aim was to establish a taxation system based on the net yield of land—an aim which, of course, required an accurate determination of this yield. He used the offices of the *ferme* whenever possible to assemble data, which were presented in tabular form, accompanied by a text, written by himself, urging that France establish an institution for the gathering and assimilating of economic data of all kinds—the data being the basis of the political economy. (It is significant of the lack of information essential to a realistic taxation policy that Lavoisier placed the national product at approximately 100 livres per capita, compared with the 150 livres estimated by Voltaire and Du Pont de Nemours. It is significant, too, of the maldistribution of national income that his own income at the time approached 40,000 livres a year, or 400 times what each person would have received had income been distributed in equal shares among the population.)

In 1785 the king appointed Lavoisier to the directorship of the Academy of Science. This meant that he was the administrative head of the body (the presidency was an honorary post), and he promptly employed the power thus given him to institute long-overdue reforms in its constitution and formal procedures. The rank of *adjoint,* the one he held when first elected, was abolished, all new members being thereafter admitted as *associés,* and every member, regardless of rank, was accorded voting rights. Their votes, moreover, were made determinative of the selection of officers, instead of being, as formerly, mere recommendations to the king, who had made the final appointments. The character of these reforms and the fact that they were carried into effect despite a formidable opposition would seem to indicate that Lavoisier, if no egalitarian (people are *not* "born equal" in ability, he would have said), certainly favored equality of opportunity in the field of activity he regarded as most important. He evidently resented here the interposition of special privilege between "natural" causes and "natural" effects.

In 1788 he helped found the Royal Society of Agriculture as a successor to the Committee for Agriculture, of which he had been secretary. His interest in agriculture had long been active. In 1778 he had bought near Blois a large estate, known as "Fréchines," which became, under his direction, an experimental farm. There the effects of different kinds and amounts of fertilizer on yields were carefully measured, wheat yields were doubled, and various new crop and tillage methods were tried out.

Thus, he lived a remarkably rich full life into the late 1780's. He had, of course, his private griefs. The sudden and premature death of his father, Jean Antoine, from apoplexy in September, 1775, struck him a hard blow. His relationship with his father had been unusually warm and close. He was similarly affected by the death of his beloved Aunt Constance in 1781. (She who had devoted her life to him left him all her considerable fortune.) No doubt these deaths accentuated his regret that he and Marie had no children, that with him the Lavoisier line came to an end. But he continued to be very happy in his marriage, fortunate in worldly goods, and vitally active in a dozen widely different fields, knowing in each of them, in varying degrees, the joys of creativity.

Lavoisier and the Politics of Revolution

Meanwhile, the political whirlwind which had begun to rise and turn over France in 1787, when Calonne's belated efforts at reform were rebuffed by an incredibly stupid and callously selfish aristocracy, increased to a destructive velocity. Some of the Notables who convened at Versailles early in 1787 had requested the king to summon the body known as the States-General, France's nearest approach to a popular Parliament, which had not met since 1614. They made the request as part of their legalistic strategy of confusion and obstruction, aimed at the defeat of Calonne's proposed reforms. It was, nevertheless, a dangerous expedient from their point of view since it might provide an effective rallying ground for popular wraths and discontents. The delegations to the States-General had historically consisted of representatives of the three estates—the nobility, the clergy, and the people—and although the last, the Third Estate, had generally been permitted more representatives than either of the other two (in 1614 the Third Estate had outnumbered the clergy by forty-one; the nobility, by fifty-seven), it had not had on this account any greater decisive power than they. On the contrary, each estate had had one vote in each delegation; this meant that the privileged orders outvoted the people by two to one. But this arrangement was not immutable, and as the initial request swelled to a popular clamor that the States-General meet at the earliest possible moment or the spring of 1789 at the latest, it was accompanied by the demand that the Third Estate be given a representation and voting power at least equal to those of the other two.

By this time the suave, glib, wily Calonne, trusted by none and hated by many, had been dismissed by the king. His place as Controller General had been taken in April, 1787, at the queen's insistence, by the reactionary Étienne Loménie de Brienne, Archbishop of Toulouse. Loménie de Brienne, who had bitterly opposed his predecessor's program in the Convocation of Notables, embraced it as a minister, hoping thereby to delay the summoning of the States-General and to ensure that when this body did at last meet, it would not be sufficiently democratic to pose a serious threat to feudal privilege and monarchical authority. As part of this strategy he acquiesced in the establishment of provincial assemblies along the general lines suggested by Calonne and, after a violent quarrel with the Parlement of Paris patched up a kind of armed truce with it and with the parlements of the provinces. But when he decided that the States-General should not meet until 1792 and when the king chose a particularly inopportune time in which to exercise arbitrary authority (he ordered the Parlement of Paris to register a loan edict it had previously refused to register, as if the Parlement were a *lit de justice*), Loménie de Brienne encountered winds of popular fury so strong that neither he nor his royal master could stand against them.

This was in August, 1788. It was the month in which the French Revolution may properly be said to have begun, for on August 8 the king was forced by popular pressures and despite the announced decision of his chief minister to summon the States-General to meet in the following May, 1789. He was also forced to suspend payments on the public debt and to return to the parlements powers of registration he had ordered stricken from them following the dispute over the loan edict. On August 24, he dismissed Loménie de Brienne, but not wholly as a result of popular pressures, since the queen's circle now opposed the unhappy minister, too, and on the following day, against his sovereign will, he recalled the relatively liberal Jacques Necker as Controller General. (Necker, a man of high ability, if somewhat lacking in moral courage, had served in this office from October, 1776, to May, 1781, when he resigned under pressure from the champions of privilege who had found even his effort at reform, mild compared with Turgot's, an outrage of their "natural rights.") Thus, the king confessed by his deeds that his regal power was far from absolute. To some as yet undetermined extent he was a subject of his subjects and must bend to their will.

Lavoisier approved of this reduction in monarchical authority. He had sat for the Third Estate in the Orléans Assembly, when the provincial assemblies were established in 1787—this despite the patent of nobility that he possessed. He had been elected as representative of the Romorantin District. Chosen secretary of the session, he was its most prominent and progressive member. He worked hard but vainly to abolish the *corvée* in Orléans Province, proposed other far-reaching tax reforms (for instance, and surprisingly, the abolition of the local "farmers of the taxes" and their replacement by tax collectors employed by the provincial government), proposed the establishment of a local branch of the Discount Bank, and prepared (in a remarkable anticipation of present-day liberalism) a scheme of state old-age and health insurance in which the poorer classes could voluntarily participate (his scheme was frustrated by the intervention of a company of speculative financiers).

He welcomed the summoning of the States-General, as did all other progressives. In a memoir to Necker on the subject he favored double representation for the Third Estate, freedom of the press, the selection of deputies by the provincial assemblies, the transformation of the States-General into a national assembly with regular future meeting times, and the establishment of a national constitution. He himself, however, acted with the nobility at Blois, instead of with the Third Estate as he had in the Orléans Assembly, when deputies to the States-General were being chosen. He was elected as an alternative deputy and prepared a manual of instructions to the delegation, but apparently he never actually served in the historic session of the States-General which opened in Versailles on May 5, 1789.

In the months preceding this opening there had been much pulling and hauling within the government between ministers who favored serious reforms and those who failed or refused to recognize that the absolute monarchy no longer existed. The latter generally won their obstructive way since Necker, at critical moments, was indecisive. Meanwhile, the decisive struggle had been initiated in an unprecedentedly full and free public political discussion. This was the struggle between the Third Estate and the two privileged orders over the proper nature and duties of the States-General, and it was carried on in the provincial assemblies, where procedures for electing deputies were decided (Lavoisier was active in it at Orléans), and in a veritable flood of pamphlets and manifestoes. The higher orders were divided on the course which should be followed, whereas the Third Estate, with minor exceptions, was united.

Nor did the struggle cease when the States-General at last met. On the contrary, it was intensified, for Necker and the king, having bowed to the popular demand that the number of Third Estate representatives be equal to that of the other two combined (actually the Third Estate was given 600 delegates out of a total of 1,155), had failed to decide whether the three orders were to meet together or separately and whether the final voting was to be done by individual ballot or by estate. These crucial questions were left up to the States-General, which wrangled over them for six weeks after the session opened. The nobles insisted on meeting separately to verify their members' credentials. So did the clergy. Thereupon the Third Estate deputies refused to act at all unless and until the others joined them in a single general meeting, with each deputy having one vote. At last, wrathfully decisive, the representatives of the Third Estate declared their meeting to be a National Assembly, declared, too, that henceforth no taxes could be imposed without their consent, and took some faltering first steps toward drafting a national constitution.

Did the king now see that his only chance of preserving any real power for the throne lay in his playing off of the commons against the privileged? He did not. He chose, instead, to exercise against the commons an arbitrary power he no longer had. He sent troops to close the hall where the Third Estate was meeting, and he more than hinted that the deputies should disperse. Instead, the rebellious commons appropriated as their meeting place an indoor tennis court in the Rue St.-François of Versailles, and there, on June 20, 1789, they swore a mighty oath: They would not disperse until a constitution for France had been drafted and established as the law of the nation, to which the king himself was subject.

Now the issue was joined. There was no turning back. The whirlwind roared over the disputed ground, its atoms including thousands upon thousands of the Parisian mob, spurred not only by long-gathered angers and hatreds and resentments but also by the fear of famine as the price of bread went up and the supply of loaves went down—a result of the disastrous harvest of 1788.

Again striving to exert a power he no longer had, the king turned to his army to quell insurrection and discovered (his commanders bluntly told him) that the army was no longer his, for it could not be trusted to fire on the people. Only the foreign mercenaries were deemed thus "loyal," thus "trustworthy," and these he ordered marched to Paris from the provinces, while outwardly he capitulated to the Third Estate, accepting "in principle" the National Assembly as a single body in which all three estates acted together. When twenty regiments ringed the capital, on July 11, he abruptly dismissed Necker, who had been siding with the Third Estate, if in typically uncertain fashion, and appointed as his chief minister the reactionary Baron de Breteuil. It became clear to all that the royal intention was to recapture power with cannon and bayonet.

July 11 was a Saturday. When news of the king's action reached Paris the next day, there was a great outpouring of people into the streets, crowds that were soon roaring in unison: "To arms! To arms!" Some of them collided with German mercenaries, who fired on them, wounding several and provoking a cry of "Massacre!" that added to the prevailing fury. Gunsmiths' shops were plundered, the French Guards broke out of the barracks to which they had been ordered confined and declared itself one with the people, and a citizens' militia was organized to patrol the streets and restore order. Relative quiet and order prevailed on Monday, July 13. This was, however, but a brief pause before the ultimate storms.

For on Tuesday, July 14, 1789, occurred the violence that history deems the decisive event of the French Revolution. On the morning of that day, rumors of an impending attack by royal troops swept through the city, and great crowds again flowed through the streets, armed with paving stones, sickles, pikestaffs, axes, and such muskets as they were able to seize from the Invalides, which they stormed. They needed powder and flints for their muskets and powder for the cannon of the citizens' militia and of the troops which had joined it, and rumor had it that large quantities of these were stored in the Bastille, having been moved there from the Arsenal (Lavoisier's home) around the corner. To the Bastille, therefore, the grim fortress prison which had long symbolized the worst of royal oppression, flowed the angry mob, demanding the fortress' surrender. The commander, Bernard René Jordan de Launay, agreed to negotiate the matter, but while he was meeting a delegation from the people, someone in the fortress, perhaps by accident, fired into the crowd. There was then no restraining the populary fury. Confused fighting developed at last into a semblance of pitched battle with cannon brought up by the French Guards and the militia, and after some hours of this the Bastille fell. Its defenders were captured. Many of these, as helpless prisoners, were murdered in the streets; among them was De Launay, whose severed head was mounted on a pike. The Bastille was torn down, stone by stone.

The great noise of its fall was echoed in the following days throughout the eastern and northwestern provinces, where mobs of angry peasants attacked châteaus, often killed the nobles (with their families) who had so brutally exploited them, and always destroyed with care the title deeds and other legal instruments which had been for them instruments of oppression.

Thus, the Old Regime was at last and forever ended. The order which was to replace it was yet to be made.

There were many people, Lavoisier among them, who saw no sharp discontinuity of substance between the end of the old and the beginning of the new. Although he deplored the mob violence that had accompanied it, Lavoisier was pleased to see the end of absolute monarchy in France, but he was among those who favored retention of the king in a constitutional monarchy modeled on England's. He said so on the floor of the Paris Assembly or Commune, to which he was elected in September, 1789, as deputy from the district of Culture St. Catherine. He said so, too, as a leading member of the '89 Club, which had the same aim (the club proposed at its meetings "to consider questions of general interest and political metaphysics without regard to party or creed"). He believed, in early 1790, that his political hopes were well on the way toward full realization.

By that time the citizens' militia of July, 1789, had become the National Guard under the command of the still youthful hero of the American War of Independence, the Marqus de Lafayette. The National Assembly governed France in the name of the king and prepared for the adoption of a national constitution. As for the king, he (with his queen and children) had been forcibly transferred from Versailles to Paris, where he was installed, virtually a prisoner of the Assembly, in the Tuileries. Lafayette's troops watched the palace closely day and night to make sure the king did not join the 200,000 aristocratic *émigrés* who had fled abroad and there sought to foment international war against their countrymen. A ringing Declaration of the Rights of Man had been adopted, France's system of legal justice had been overhauled, and France's fiscal system—thanks in part to the energy and talents which Lavoisier exercised in his capacity as a governor of the Discount Bank—was remodeled along lines more rational than those which had prevailed.

"We regard the Revolution as finished, irrevocably," he wrote to Benjamin Franklin in February, 1790.[2] He recognized no real danger from the political right. "There is still a weak royalist party . . . ," he wrote, but the "constitutional party . . . is numerous, including among its members the intelligent and enlightened citizens." More ominous was the threat from the left: "The moderates who have kept their heads during the excitement think that circumstances have already carried us too far, that it is a pity to have stirred up the people so, that it is imprudent to place in power those who ought to obey, and that it is to be feared that the new constitution is meeting with opposition from those for whom it is made."

He had in mind the rise, slow as yet, of the radical Jacobin Club, whose aim was not to reform the old, but to destroy it utterly and build wholly anew. Nothing less than a French republic of the most extreme democracy would satisfy these fire-eating Jacobins. Lavoisier regarded them with distaste and unease, but not, as yet, with fear.

The Revolution Kills Lavoisier

Two events, which may in a sense have been related, destroyed in 1791 the "finished" revolution to which such "enlightened moderates" as Lavoisier were committed. One was the death in early April of the Comte de Mirabeau. A giant of political intelligence and energy, unscrupulous in his personal ambitions (Necker fell before him) but dreaming a great dream for France, Mirabeau had dominated the National Assembly so far as any one man could. Beloved of the people, he was also influential to a degree with king and queen, although most royalists in their incredible selfishness and stupidity were his bitter enemies; he provided in his person a bridge over which that best worth preserving in the Old Regime could be carried across the gulf of revolution into the new France. With Mirabeau gone, the vital force which had done most to restrain the extremists of right and left was gone. He himself had been well aware of his role. "When I am gone," said he on his deathbed, "they will know what the value of me was. The miseries I have held back will burst from all sides on France."

The second event was the secret flight of the king, the queen, and their two children from the Tuileries, from Paris, almost from France onto foreign soil, where they might have headed invading armies of French *émigrés* and foreign monarchs. This was on the night of June 20 and through the long day of June 21, the longest day of 1791. The royal party was recognized that evening in a small town in the Argonne and captured a few hours later at Varennes, whence they were returned as prisoners to Paris, convicted in the eyes of all as enemies of their own people and traitors to the constitution they had sworn they would uphold. Had Mirabeau been alive, he would have done his best to dissuade the royal couple from this madness. Probably he would have succeeded. As it was, the last chance to realize the hopes of the "enlightened moderates" was lost: The king simply could not be trusted.

On July 17, about three weeks after the captive royal family had been returned to the Tuileries, a great crowd of republicans assembled on the Champ-de-Mars to sign a petition demanding that the National Assembly remove Louis from the throne for traitorous activities (his "crime has been proved") and that "a new constituent body" be established to "proceed in a genuinely national manner to try the criminal; above all, to replace him, and to organize a new executive power." The crowd was unarmed.

Nevertheless, it was fired on by municipal troops. A dozen fell dead, three dozen were wounded, and for several weeks thereafter the Assembly used the National Guard, under martial law, to suppress what the Minister of Justice termed "a mob of rebels," whose "only objects" were "murder, pillage, disorder, and anarchy, which they... [call] liberty." The queen was, of course, pleased by this severity. "I have seen with pleasure the determination and courage with which you... have upheld the monarchy," she wrote to the Minister of Justice. But popular faith in the Assembly was by this action irrevocably destroyed, and republicanism, augmented in numbers, was inflamed in its passions.

It was further augmented and inflamed by the actions of foreign sovereigns during the following months. Egged on by French *émigrés* and their own outraged egoism, these foolish men "ordered" the French people to restore to Louis his full "rights" as absolute monarch or suffer grave consequences. The natural if imprudent response of the French was to force Louis to declare war on his friends in Austria, a war in which Prussia was soon allied with Austria and which went so badly for France that the king and queen and their supporters were popularly believed to be subverting French arms and betraying them through secret communication with the enemy. Jacobinism, led by Marat, Danton, Robespierre, fed on such suspicious fears and grew great. On August 10 a Parisian mob invaded the Tuileries, massacred the royal bodyguard, and forced the royal family to flee for their lives to the nearby riding academy where the National Assembly, in a fearful chaos of a session, was about to transform itself into the much more radical National Convention. Incarcerated in Temple Prison, royalty was thereafter a prisoner of the Convention. On August 20, Lafayette, both symbol and leader of moderation, deserted his command at the front and crossed the frontier, rather than serve the new Jacobin government. On September 2 angry and fearful mobs, encouraged by Jacobin leaders, invaded prisons where political prisoners were being held and massacred indiscriminately some 2,000 men and women. On September 20 a battle was fought at Valmy, halting the Prussian invaders. On the following day the formal abolition of royalty was voted by the National Convention, and on the day after that, September 22, the French Republic was declared established.

It was a republic ringed by enemies and, as a result, soon transformed into dictatorship. "We must establish the despotism of liberty to crush the despotism of kings," explained Marat. Of liberty's despotism the prime symbol and agent became ultimately the guillotine set up in the newly named Place de la Révolution (formerly the Place de Louis Quinze), where was sent for execution on January 21, 1793, the deposed king, now dubbed plain Citizen Louis Capet, condemned for treason. ("Allied kings threaten us," cried the leonine Danton on this occasion, "and we hurl at their feet as a gage of battle the head of a king!") A haggard Marie Antoinette was sent to the guillotine in October of that year. Multitudes followed, as there was decreed—in the name of "Liberty, Equality, and Fraternity"—a Reign of Terror. Moderates who (in Lavoisier's words) had "kept their heads during the excitement" of 1789 and 1790 were no longer able to do so, as the Revolution began to devour those who had made it. Their severed heads fell by the scores, by the hundreds into the wicker baskets of Sanson, the public executioner, all through 1793 and the first half of 1794. Among them was the head of Lavoisier.

So long as moderation ruled at all in the highest councils of France, the unique talents of the great scientist as public servant continued to be made use of. He was appointed to the six-man board of the newly organized National Treasury in 1791, ostentatiously refusing for this service a salary, which assuredly he did not need. (He published in the *Moniteur* an all too obviously fawning letter, in which he said: "The income I enjoy as Commissioner of Powders, for the very reason that it is modest, is in conformity with my manner of living, my tastes and needs; at a time when many citizens are losing their wordly goods I could not consent to profit by a double salary.") As a member of this board, he was typically efficient and effective. He is said to have established a system of accounting so swiftly precise "that one knew the condition of the treasury day by day." [3] In January, 1792, through Pierre Du Pont de Nemours, whom he had launched in the publishing business the year before with a loan of some 710,000 livres, he published a pamphlet, *De l'Etat des Finances de France* ("On the State of the Finances of France"), wherein he said characteristically: "At a time when all things good and bad are alike exaggerated... it is advisable to discuss the finances of the nation dispassionately and with rigorous arithmetic." He proceeded to do so. At about this time he wrote to the Minister of Interior that although "payments to the treasury on land and [in] personal taxes are extremely small ... we may be dragged into war by the too precipitate action of the Assembly. ..." He regarded the impending event as an instance of "what happens in all popular governments: moderation is not the rule. ..." He could only hope that "a constitution philosophically sound" would bring "calmness." A month later, in February, 1792, he resigned his Treasury post.

More interesting to us, being more revealing of the wide range of his interests and of the creative mental power he applied to each of them, was his service on the advisory board of the Bureau of Arts and Crafts, established in 1791. He prepared for presentation to the National Convention in 1793, on behalf of the bureau, a report entitled *Réflexions sur l'Instruction Publique* ("Reflections on Public Instruction") wherein he anticipated (although following the general principles of Condorcet) much of the theory of education which animated the development of America's land-grant colleges in the 1860's and 1870's and, to a degree, the progressivism of John Dewey in the twentieth century. Lavoisier proposed a system of universal free education as "a duty that society owes to the child" and outlined in detail curricula for primary and secondary schools, suggesting also (a then highly original suggestion) the establishment of upper level vocational schools to serve "the interest of . . . the [industrial] classes." He was especially concerned to realize the educative values of science while avoiding the evils of excessive specialization. He insisted on the essential unity of all knowledge. "We must not encourage exclusively certain parts of education and ignore others," he wrote. "The arts, the sciences, and literature are bound together with invisible ties which cannot be broken with impunity."

His most useful public service during this period—a service from which mankind continues to benefit—was as a member of a committee of the Academy set up in 1790 for the purpose of developing a uniform system of weights and measures for the nation. In August, 1793, when the Academy was abolished by the Committee on Public Instruction, which condemned it as a vestige of the Old Regime despite the valiant efforts to save it made by Lavoisier as its last active director, the measuration committee continued its work as the Government Commission on Weights and Measures. At the outset the Academy had sought to enlist the Royal Society of London in the enterprise, so that the development would be international, but the effort failed—a grave misfortune, since the metric system resulting from the Frenchmen's work, used now everywhere in science, is in every respect superior to that which the English-speaking peoples continue to employ in their daily lives. Lavoisier's specific contributions to the new system included a collaboration with other scientists in a precise determination of the density of distilled water, used as the basic unit of weight, and of the relative expansions of copper and platinum, used as the basic unit of length.

He was at work on this project when, on November 28, 1793, he was arrested "by order of the police." He must have known for many months that his life was endangered by the Terror. So many of his friends and associates had been killed by it, often with less excuse than could be found by fanatic republicans for his own extinction. He must have realized, too, that three specific acts in his past, each inspired by honorable motives, would now rise up, as if they were the most heinous crimes, and cry through Jacobin mouths for his blood.

One was his proposal as a farmer-general years before that a tax wall be built around Paris to prevent the smuggling of produce into the capital, thus protecting honest traders. The wall was built at public expense by one Le Doux, who fattened on what was evidently a cost-plus contract by constructing a needlessly elaborate stone barricade at a price of no less than 30,000,000 livres. The Parisian populace, rich and poor alike, was outraged—and not only by the excessive cost. It was widely believed that the wall prevented a natural circulation of air so that bad air was kept in Paris and pure air out. "All the world is assured that M. Lavoisier ... is the beneficent patriot to whom we owe this ingenious and salutary imprisonment of the capital of France," said, in bitter irony, an anonymous pamphlet that had wide circulation. "The *Ferme* may

erect a monument to him [upon his death] for this invention, but the Academy is ashamed of [or blushes for] his
membership in the *Ferme*. . . ." A marshal of France gave
it as his succinct opinion that Lavoisier "ought to be
hanged."

Another act, dangerous to his life at the time, was performed in his capacity as a powder commissioner. Some
low-grade industrial powder was being shipped from Metz
to Rouen and Nantes for storage before being sold abroad,
in August, 1789, when it was seized by excited Revolutionary vigilantes and diverted to the Arsenal of Paris.
There it occupied magazine space that should have been
filled with musket powder. Accordingly, Lavoisier sought
and obtained from the office of General Lafayette, com-
mandant of the National Guard, permission to have the
industrial powder shipped to Essones for storage, an equal
amount of musket powder being then shipped back from
Essones to the Arsenal. Actually the permit for this was
signed, not by Lafayette, but by his chief of staff, the
Marquis de la Salle, and when angrily suspicious citizens
called on Lafayette to protest the reloading of the river
barge with powder they had "saved" for the Revolution,
Lafayette fed their anger and suspicion by denying that
any permit had been issued. There followed an ugly mob
scene wherein the lives of Lavoisier, La Salle, and others
were very seriously threatened before the confused situation could at last be clarified. There remained, even then,
a black mark (another one) against Lavoisier's name: He
continued to be suspected of traitorous sentiments, if not
of overt treason.

The *third* of the three acts, although probably the most
dangerous now of all, carried with it at the time it occurred
no slightest premonition of personal danger. How could
he have supposed in 1780 that Jean Paul Marat, a Swiss
medical doctor of about Lavoisier's age—a man of whom

he had never heard before and who now published scientific work of (in Lavoisier's opinion) contemptible quality —was destined to become for a time the most powerful political figure in France, holding in his hands the power of life or death over men and institutions? Had Lavoisier suspected it, he might in common prudence have acted otherwise than he did. The Swiss doctor established a lucrative medical practice in Paris, but not without resort to quackery; published a memoir, influenced by Mesmerism, on "medical electricity" (*Recherches sur l'électricité médicale*, 1783); won a prize from the Rouen Academy for an essay on new discoveries regarding light (*Nouvelles découvertes sur la lumière*, 1783); translated Newton's *Optics* into French; and published (in 1780) a scientific work he hoped would win him election to the Academy, a memoir entitled *Recherches physiques de la feu* ("Physical Researches on Fire"). The latter was his undoing. Earlier, several influential academicians—among them Le Roy and Condorcet—had favored his election, but the work on fire brought Lavoisier out adamantly against him, for it presented, in the kind of vague, loose, speculative language that Lavoisier most deplored and on the basis of no valid experimental evidence, a theory of combustion contrary to Lavoisier's. When a Paris journal published a notice (submitted by Marat?) that the memoir had been formally approved by the Academy, Lavoisier promptly, publicly, and contemptuously denied it. The work was devoid of merit, he indicated; the Academy would never place on it its stamp of approval. Marat, reading this, knew that he would never become an academician. The Swiss doctor thereafter hated Lavoisier personally and identified the Academy with the worst evils of ancient privilege.

It was as a rabble-rousing journalist, the most powerful figure in the so-called Fourth Estate with his newspaper *L'Ami du peuple* ("The Friend of the People"), that

Marat came to the forefront of Jacobinism as the Revolution developed. It was in the issue of January 27, 1791, that *L'Ami du peuple* launched the attack on Lavoisier which ultimately proved fatal. "I denounce to you the coryphaeus of charlatans the sieur Lavoisier, son of a land-grabber, pupil of the Geneva stock-jobber, Farmer-General, controller of gunpowder and saltpeter, governor of the Discount Bank, secretary to the King, member of the Academy of Sciences," wrote Marat. "Would you believe that this little gentleman, who enjoys an income of 40,000 livres and whose only claim to public recognition is that he put Paris in prison by cutting off the fresh air with a wall that cost the poor 33 millions and that he removed the powder from the Arsenal to the Bastille on the night of July 12 and 13 [he did attempt to do so], is engaged on a devilish intrigue to get himself elected an administrator of the department of Paris? . . . Would to heaven he had been strung to the lamp-post on August 6. Then the electors of la Culture would not need to blush for having nominated him." [4] Subsequently, in newspaper and pamphlet, Marat attacked other academicians, accusing them of misusing for private pleasures money granted them for research, but his most venomous attacks were always aimed at Lavoisier.

The specific charge leading to Lavoisier's arrest and imprisonment at Port Libre (formerly the Convent of Port-Royal) was that he and his former colleagues of the *ferme générale,* which had been abolished by the National Assembly in March, 1791, had defrauded the nation of 400,000,000 livres. These colleagues—thirty-one of them, including his father-in-law, Jacques Paulze—were imprisoned with Lavoisier while a committee, headed by the deputy André Dupin, investigated the charge. They were moved to the former office building of the farm, now converted into a prison for them, in December, 1793, and were

THE CAUTIONARY SCIENTISTS   214

there informed, in the following month, that all their property had been confiscated and that their homes would be sold by the state. (Lavoisier's home was then in the Boulevard de la Madeleine; he had moved from the Arsenal after his forced resignation from the powder commission in early 1792.) Several weeks later Dupin's committee completed its "investigation." The amount of money the farmers-general were alleged to have stolen was revised downward from 400,000,000 to 130,000,000, but Dupin was now demanding that the accused be tried as enemies of the state before the dreaded Revolutionary Tribunal.

Events thereafter spiraled relentlessly down toward nameless graves in the cemetery of La Madeleine for twenty-eight of the accused. There was a brief moment of slender hope for Lavoisier as the spring of 1794 came on. The pharmacist from whom Lavoisier had purchased his laboratory chemicals was acquainted with Dupin's sister-in-law, a woman of easy virtue, and through her he managed to persuade Dupin to separate the scientist from the other farmers, putting him in a different prison, and to eliminate from the final report all that might condemn him. The deputy insisted, however, that Mme. Lavoisier call on him in prison to beg this favor, instead of proceeding, as she had heretofore done, through her aristocratic friends. She came. But instead of pleading for her husband's life, as the sadistic Dupin clearly expected her to do, she was haughty and demanding. Only scoundrels could accuse her husband, who was an innocent man; all the accused, including her father, were innocent men; her husband would be dishonored if his case was separated from the rest. She demanded that all be set free—and so slammed shut (for Dupin was infuriated by her) the last possible door for her husband's escape.

Dupin presented his report to the National Convention on May 5, 1794, and obtained, with no single dissenting vote, a decree that the "farmers be brought to judgment before the Revolutionary Tribunal." Already he had helped the attorney general of the tribunal prepare the formal charge sheets. That night the prisoners were transferred to the Conciergerie, where Lavoisier, his father-in-law, and one other man occupied the cell in which Marie Antoinette had spent her last hours before entering the tumbril. Here, the next day, he wrote his last letter, addressed to a beloved cousin but intended for "all those who love me." He would at least "die in good health," he wrote, and be spared "the inconvenience of old age," having had a "passably long career and a happy one." He believed that his untimely passing would be "accompanied by some regrets" and his memory "perhaps by some glory."

At one o'clock the next morning, the charge sheets were presented to the thirty-two prisoners, who were unable to read them in the dark. At dawn all save one of the thirty-two (that one had been transferred to another prison through the influence of friends) were taken to an anteroom of the tribunal where four court-appointed defenders were granted just fifteen minutes in which to prepare their obviously futile defenses. At ten o'clock, under youthful Judge Coffinhal, the farcical trial began. Sometime during it a report from the Bureau of Arts and Crafts was presented in evidence of scientist Lavoisier's past services and present value to the state. Coffinhal glanced at it. "The Republic," he is reported then to have said contemptuously, "... the Republic has no need for scientists. ..." A little later the judge summed up the presented evidence and invented some of his own, its nature demanding capital punishment, as he charged the jury. "Has there been a plot against the people tending to favor the enemies of France by excising, extorting, exacting from the people, by adding water to tobacco ..., by retarding the warfare of the nation against despots who rise against the Republic?" Thus asked Coffinhal, and the jury promptly, dutifully, unanimously replied, "Yes!" The accused were guilty —all save three who had been excused at the opening of the trial because they had not been connected with the *ferme générale* during the period when the crimes were perpetrated. The condemned were to suffer death "within forty-eight hours." They suffered it within four.

The sentence was pronounced in midafternoon, and the prisoners returned to the Conciergerie. At five o'clock they were loaded into tumbrils at the prison gate, Lavoisier standing beside Paulze in one of them. The shadows were long across the Place de la Révolution in the lowering sun as Lavoisier and the twenty-seven others dismounted and then, one by one, climbed the steps of the scaffold and laid their bared necks under the bloodstained knife. Paulze was the third of the condemned to do so, Lavoisier the fourth. The time was between five and six o'clock in the afternoon of May 8, 1794.

Academician Joseph Louis Lagrange, mathematician, learned of Lavoisier's death the next day. "Only a moment to cut off his head," said he, "and perhaps a hundred years before we grow another like it!"

The Terror ended a few months later, choked to death on its own blood. In the reaction, the revulsion that followed, the state made such efforts as could still be made to correct flagrant injustices. A careful audit of *ferme générale* accounts revealed none of the fraud that had been alleged. Indeed, far from owing the state 130,000,000 livres, the farmers-general were owed 8,000,000 by the state, according to the terms of the contract. Mme. Lavoisier and the other heirs made, wisely, no effort to collect these millions, having by that time had returned to them the property that had been confiscated. She, Lavoisier's widow, then became one of the wealthiest women in Paris.

She was also one of the coldest and haughtiest, all warmth and spontaneous gaiety having been cut out of her by the knife that had severed her husband's neck. Widower Pierre Du Pont de Nemours, who had long loved her and to whom Lavoisier had chiefly entrusted her when he knew himself to be in fatal danger, became her suitor and was rejected. He was fortunate. She married, instead, Count Rumford, who had been born plain Benjamin Thompson on a Massachusetts farm but who now considered himself to be one of the most aristocratic of Continental aristocrats. He was a count of the Holy Roman Empire; he was also a great and famous scientist. He is famous still in history as the man who destroyed the mythical "caloric," which Lavoisier had deemed an element, as effectively as Lavoisier had destroyed the mythical "phlogiston." Rumford proved that heat is energy. But although he mastered a problem that had defeated the great chemist, he was never able to master the chemist's widow. Within a year after his marriage he called his wife a "female dragon," she poured boiling water on his prized roses, and all Paris talked and laughed about their violent public quarrels. Within two years they had agreed to live apart. She died at the age of seventy-six, in Paris, on February 10, 1836.

6. *Doctor Priestley Dies in Exile*

Birmingham and the Lunar Society

When the French Revolution began, Joseph Priestley
was living in the rising industrial town of Birmingham.
He had been living there for nine years, his connection
with Lord Shelburne having been severed in 1780.

Although the specific cause of the break between the
two men is now unknown and, indeed, seems to have been
unknown to Priestley himself, the general reasons are easily
surmised. Shelburne, as has been indicated, was a man difficult to know and still more difficult to love. By nature a
secretive man—reluctant, if not unable, to confide in others
—he inspired distrust for this reason alone. People could
not be sure where they stood with him; their lack of certainty on this score bred uneasiness, if not actual anxiety,
in their relationships with him, and this in turn bred a
personal resentment of him. He took, they felt, an unfair
advantage. He was psychologically unjust. Priestley, on
the other hand, was frank and open and trusting to a fault.

Clothed in transparent honesty, he was reluctant, if not unable, to prevent a complete revelation of himself and of his opinion on every subject (he *had* an opinion on every subject); the simple integrity of his soul showed through all that he said and did. It was inevitable that two such contradictory natures would sooner or later grate on one another.

Nor were there lacking more particular reasons that Shelburne would become dissatisfied with the relationship. When Priestley was first asked to come to Bowood, his political views were already well known; they were not basically incompatible with Shelburne's, although Priestley favored independence for the American Colonies while Shelburne still opposed it. Priestley's highly controversial religious views were even better known, and although Shelburne seems to have regarded theological controversy as a boring waste of time and energy, he raised no objection to Priestley's indulging in it. Thus, in the original agreement between the two men no restriction whatever was placed on Priestley's freedom to speak and write on whatever subject he pleased. Out of respect for his patron, he did refrain from publishing on politics, as Shelburne, at first living in retirement on his estate, was drawn again more and more into public political life. No such consideration inhibited his publications on religious subjects, although it was soon clear that they did more harm to his patron's political ambitions than Priestley's politics, freely published, could have done.

Especially was this true of the *Disquisitions relating to Matter and Spirit* (published in 1777). In it Priestley defined man and the universe in wholly materialistic, mechanistic terms and came dangerously close to defining God in the same way. The deity to him was but a synonym for the "intelligent first cause" of all that is or can become. We suppose that God exists because there must be a "first cause," but "of the nature of the *existence* of this primary cause, concerning which we know nothing but by its *effects,* we cannot have any conception." From this it followed that God was the author of all evil, as well as of all good, although Priestley denied that this indicated that God was no perfect being. What it indicated, said he, is that concepts of good and evil that apply to finite and therefore fallible minds do not apply to omniscience, which sees how the infliction of evil can produce good.

The outcry that greeted this publication was, according to Priestley, "such as could hardly be imagined." In fact, it was anticipated by some of his good friends who tried to dissuade him from the publication of it and of later writings in the same field. One such friend (Benjamin Vaughan, who had been a boarding student of Priestley's when the latter was at Warrington and who later emigrated with his brother, Samuel, Jr., to Hallowell, Maine) complained afterward that "I could only stop publication for six months, though it was to hurt his patron with the public and the court, appear when it would." Some of the outcry was good-natured. Priestley himself enjoyed an epitaph for his tombstone composed by the Welsh poet David Davis:

> Here lies at rest,
> In oaken chest,
>> Together packed most nicely,
> The bones and brains,
> Flesh, blood and veins
>> And soul of Dr. Priestley.

But most of the comments, appearing in newspapers and magazines throughout Britain, as well as in numerous pamphlets, were virulently hostile. The worst anticipations of Shelburne's political followers were realized. Priestley was, to all intents and purposes, an atheist, who subverted the moral order; he was a menace to society; and any man who patronized so dangerous a heretic and radical should not be trusted with political power.

One can hardly blame Shelburne for wishing to rid himself of so serious a political liability, especially in the late 1770's, when it became evident that his consistent opposition to George III's American policy, a policy executed at the time through the ministry of Lord North, might lead him to the highest political office in the aftermath of disaster in the French and American wars. (It did so, as a matter of fact, in 1782, when he became the Prime Minister who, during a stormy eight months, negotiated peace with France and with the independent United States.) Characteristically, however, Shelburne did not disclose frankly to Priestley his wish to alter their relationship. Priestley later wrote that "about two years before I left him I perceived evident marks of dissatisfaction, though I never understood the cause of it...." Early in 1780 Shelburne let it be known that he contemplated setting up his erstwhile librarian in an Irish establishment. Priestley, hearing of this and hurt by it, concluded that his patron wished to be rid of him. He therefore suggested to Shelburne that they part according to the terms of their original agreement, whereby Priestley received a lifetime annuity of 150 pounds. Shelburne promptly agreed. "When I left him," wrote Priestley, "I asked him if he had any fault to find in my conduct, and he said *none*." Nevertheless, when he wished to call on Shelburne in London a few months later, he was given to understand that his old patron did not wish to see him. Years later, after Shelburne's political career had ended and he had been created Marquess of Lansdowne, he tried to restore his former relationship with Priestley and was refused, although Priestley remained forever grateful to his patron and often published his gratitude.

At the suggestion of John Wilkinson, his brother-in-law, Priestley moved to Birmingham in the autumn of 1780, after some months in London. There were excellent reasons for his doing so. He wished to resume his active ministry—he had been separated from it for seven years—and was offered the ministry of the Presbyterian congregation of Birmingham's New Meetinghouse, reputed to be the most liberal congregation in England. As an industrial town, Birmingham could provide excellent workmen and equipment for his scientific experiments. Most important of all was the presence there, or nearby, of Wilkinson himself and of Wilkinson's and Priestley's good friends, Matthew Boulton and James Watt, who were in partnership to manufacture Watt's steam engine (Wilkinson cast in his ironworks "the 18-inch cylinder which enabled Watt's engine to run smoothly, and the first engine made by . . . [Boulton and Watt] was to his order" [1]); Josiah Wedgwood, the great and scientifically minded pottery manufacturer; and Erasmus Darwin, the highly successful medical practitioner, whose interests were both literary and scientific. (Darwin was the paternal, Wedgwood the maternal, grandfather of Charles Darwin, whose theory of evolution was to some extent anticipated in Erasmus Darwin's *Zoonomia*) (1794-96).

Boulton and Darwin had formed, some fourteen years before, an informal group of a dozen or so men who were interested in natural science and literature, primarily the former. They met in one another's houses once a month on the Monday nearest the full moon, so that the members would have moonlight by which to return to their homes—hence, the name Lunar Society, which is famous in English intellectual history. It was, wrote Richard Lovell Edgeworth in his *Memoirs* (1820), "such a society as few men have had the good fortune to live with; such an assemblage of friends as fewer still have had the happiness to possess . . .

through life." Some of the flavor of the meetings is suggested by a note Darwin wrote Boulton on an occasion when the physician's medical duties prevented his attendance. "I am sorry the infernal divinities who visit mankind with diseases ... should have prevented my seeing all you great men," he wrote. "Lord! what inventions, what wit, what rhetoric, metaphysical, mechanical, and pyrotechnical, will be on the wing, bandied like a shuttlecock from one to another of your troop of philosophers! while poor I ... , imprisoned in a post-chaise, am joggled, and jostled, and bump'd, and bruised along the King's high road, to make war upon a stomach-ache or a fever!" A letter written sometime later by Watt to Darwin said:

> I beg that you impress on your memory the idea that you promised to dine with sundry men of learning at my house on Monday next, and that you will realize the idea. For your encouragement there is a new book to cut up, and it is to be determined whether or not heat is a compound of phlogiston and empyreal air, and whether a mirror can reflect the heat of the fire. I give you a friendly warning that you may be found wanting whichever opinion you may adopt on the latter question; therefore be cautious. If you are meek and humble, perhaps you may be told what light is made of, and also how to make it, and the theory proved by synthesis and analysis.[2]

The Lunar Society accorded Priestley an enthusiastic welcome when he arrived in Birmingham. He became at once a leading member and chemistry thereafter became the chief subject of discussion at society meetings. "I dined yesterday at the Lunar Society (Keir's house)," Watt wrote to Boulton soon after Priestley had arrived; "there was Blair, Priestley, Withering, Galton, and an American 'rebel,' Mr. Collins. Nothing new except that some of my white Spathos Iron ore was found to contain more air than any ore Priestley had ever tried, and, what is singular, it contains no common air, but is part fixable and part inflammable." There is no doubt that the society contributed much to Priestley's personal happiness (he was happier in Birmingham than he had been anywhere before) and to his intellectual stimulation, although his greatest work in science was now behind him. He later wrote of it: "We had nothing to do with the *religious* or political principles of each other; we were united by a common love of *science,* which we thought sufficient to bring together persons of all distinctions—Christians, Jews, Mohammedans and heathen, Monarchists and Republicans."

Priestley's home in Birmingham—actually, a little way outside what were then the limits of the town—was at Fairhill. The house, if far from grand, was very handsome and pleasant, with "a fine meadow on the one side and a delightful garden on the other." The quotation is from the memoirs of the French geologist Barthélemy Faujas de Saint-Fond,[3] who visited Fairhill sometime in the 1780's and who, writing of this visit, went on to extol "the most perfect neatness in every thing connected with this house, both without and within it." He was reminded of "those snug houses so often to be met with in Holland." Priestley's laboratory was in a building separate from the house, "to avoid the danger of fire," and consisted "of several apartments on the ground floor." Saint-Fond was particularly struck by Priestley's "ingenious apparatus for making experiments on inflammable gas extracted from iron and water reduced to vapor." He was also impressed by Priestley's library. He noted:

> The learned possessor employs himself in a variety of studies: History, Moral Philosophy and Religion have all in their turn engaged his pen. An active, intelligent mind and a natural avidity for knowledge gave him a passion for experimental philosophy; but the sensibility and gentleness of his disposition have sometimes directed his attention

to pious and philanthropic studies, which do honor to the goodness of his heart, since they always have for their object the happiness of mankind.

Priestley spent at least as many laborious hours in his library at Fairhill as he did in his laboratory. The fifth volume of his work *Experiments and Observations* appeared the year after his removal to Birmingham, but virtually all (if not quite all) the experiments reported therein had been performed at Calne. The sixth and last volume of this work did not appear until 1786 and is more interesting to the historian of science for its revealing errors of induction than for the new truths it reported. (The first paper, entitled "Experiments Relating to Phlogiston," aimed at discrediting Lavoisier by "proving" experimentally that "phlogiston" was actually "inflammable air.") He himself insisted that the long delay in the publication of the final volume was due, not to the time he had "thrown away" in theological controversy, as some had "complained," but to the unprecedented time-consuming difficulty of the experiments he reported and of the argument he based on them. He asserted: "The labor and attention necessary to enable me to write single paragraphs in this work have been more than requisite to compose whole sections or chapters of the former. . . ." It is significant, however, that this assertion appeared in a Preface whose prevailing tone is defensive, the main defense resting on the alleged "superior dignity and importance of *theological studies* to any other whatever."

In 1780 he published the first part of *Letters to a Philosophical Unbeliever* (the last part appeared in 1787), wherein he attempted with doubtful success to defend what he called "natural religion" against the corrosive skepticism of David Hume. In 1782 he published a *History of the Corruptions of Christianity*, which made a direct attack on many of the central beliefs of orthodoxy, particularly on the doctrine of the Trinity, by showing, or attempting to show, how they had developed historically long after Christianity had been first established and how logically absurd they were. In 1786 he published a *History of the Early Opinions Concerning Jesus Christ,* considered by many to be his best book; in it he set out to prove that the doctrine of the Trinity was not according to Scripture, but that even if it were, it would remain so ridiculous that no reasonable man could possibly accept it. His main argument here was one he had developed as long ago as 1771 in the following words: "Things *above* our reason may, for anything that we know to the contrary, be true, but things expressly *contrary* to our reason, as that *three* should be *one,* or *one three,* can never appear to be so." The Scriptures, he had long insisted, must be interpreted in the light of reason, for no man can truly believe "on any authority . . . what is, in the nature of things, *impossible*."

Each of these three publications, especially the last two, provoked a storm of controversy, into which Priestley plunged happily. (He was a great believer in controversy as a means of destroying error and revealing truth, and he loved the excitement of intellectual battle.) He was again attacked in dozens of pamphlets and periodicals, denounced by name in a hundred pulpits, and made the subject of hostile comment in the House of Commons. Principal leader of this attack was Samuel Horsley, Archdeacon of St. Albans. In the manner generally characteristic of the upholders of orthodoxy in any field, Horsley devoted himself, not to refuting Priestley's arguments, but to denying Priestley's competency to argue. He said frankly that he aimed "to destroy the writer's credit and the authority of his name; which the fame of certain lucky discoveries in the prosecution of physical experiments had set high in popular esteem." He believed he had done so, and no doubt *had* done so with the majority, when, after

some months of tract and countertract, he was made a
bishop and indicated that henceforth he would consider
public dispute with Priestley to be beneath his dignity.

Benjamin Franklin, who must have heard echoes of this
sound and fury all the way across the Atlantic, wrote from
America to a mutual friend of his and Priestley's in October, 1788:

> Remember me affectionately to . . . the honest heretic,
> Dr. Priestley. I do not call him honest by way of distinc-
> tion, for I think all the heretics I have known have been
> virtuous men. They have the virtue of fortitude, or they
> would not venture to own their heresy; and they cannot
> afford to be deficient in any of the other virtues, as that
> would give advantage to their many enemies; and they have
> not, like orthodox sinners, such a number of friends to
> excuse or justify them. Do not, however, mistake me. It is
> not to my good friend's heresy that I impute his honesty.
> On the contrary 'tis his honesty that has brought upon
> him the character of heretic.[4]

But such admiration was by then rare in the public at
large. Most of the populace regarded Priestley as an agent
of the Devil, and this feeling against him, continuously
fed by the spokesmen for political conservatism and religious orthodoxy, was piled higher and higher all through
the 1780's. It was a highly inflammable material. A spark
might ignite it.

The Honest Heretic and the French Revolution

That English Dissenters should greet with enthusiasm
the advent of the French Revolution was perfectly predictable. Under the Test and Corporation Acts they continued to be denied the full rights of citizens, being barred
from government office and from admission to Oxford,
Cambridge, and the other established seats of learning.

They saw in France the abolition of religious intolerance, the assurance of complete equality of all faiths before the law, and were encouraged to hope that the French example would promote the swift repeal of English laws which penalized them. (The Test and Corporation Acts were not in fact repealed until 1828.) For the same reason, of course, most high English churchmen viewed the events in France with a disapproval which soon became fear and, as the inevitable offspring of fear, a virulent hatred of those of their countrymen who espoused the Revolutionary cause.

That Joseph Priestley should especially welcome the French revolt was also perfectly predictable. He was that most extreme form of Dissenter, a Unitarian—a heretic even to most of those who remained outside the Established Church—and no one in all England was more passionately committed than he to unmitigated human freedom. The French slogan of "Liberty, Equality, and Fraternity" had for him, therefore, a special appeal.

> His chemical pursuits were for a time forgotten, and he wrote and preached of human brotherhood and of the downfall of tyranny and priestcraft [wrote Samuel Smiles]. He hailed with delight the successive acts of the National Assembly—abolishing monarchy, nobility, church, corporations, and other long-established institutions. He had already been long and hotly engaged in polemical discussions with the local clergy on disputed points of faith; and now he addressed a larger audience in a work which he published in answer to Mr. Burke's famous attack on the "French Revolution." [5]

The latter, Edmund Burke's *Reflections on the Revolution in France and on the Proceedings of Certain Societies in London Relative to That Event,* had as its immediate incitement a sermon preached by Dr. Richard Price. Price was not only one of Priestley's best and oldest friends but also a fellow Unitarian and a member of the Royal Society. Although the two men were by now in wide disagreement on subjects of metaphysics and moral philosophy, they were as one in their view of the French events of 1789. There was in London at the time a so-called Revolution Society, most of whose members (but by no means all) were Dissenters. It had been established to perpetuate the memory of England's Glorious Revolution of 1688, when James II, who had sought to force England back into Roman Catholicism, was overthrown. Its annual custom was to hold a celebration on November 5, the anniversary of the landing in England of William of Orange, and in 1789 the members decided that the celebration should be in honor of Revolutionary France. Price, asked to give the sermon, did so under the title of "The Love of Our Country," stressing that the English Revolution of 1688 remained incomplete so long as the Test Acts were in force and Parliament remained unrepresentative of the people and thanking God that 30,000,000 Frenchmen had spurned slavery.

Burke, reading this sermon, was moved to reply in the form of "a letter intended to have been sent to a gentleman in Paris." He disagreed heatedly and eloquently with Dr. Price's assumption that the French events of 1789 were of a nature similar to the English events of 1688. They were, said he, radically different. He recognized the English Revolution as an orderly transfer of power from the Crown to the people, carried out within a framework of institutionalized tradition, which remained essentially unchanged. The French Revolution, on the other hand, was a complete break with the past. No institutions remained, or would long remain, which could restrain the bloody licentiousness of the mob. (In this he showed prescience, for he wrote during the relatively mild first year of the French upheaval, well before the Jacobins had captured power.) He bemoaned the loss of the elegance of manner and sophistication of intellect which seemed to him to distinguish France's Old Regime. ("He pities the plumage but forgets the dying bird," Thomas Paine in his answering *Rights of Man*.) He abhorred the rise to supreme power of rude common men, who were unfit for the government of themselves, much less of a great state. For the French National Assembly he had nothing but angry scorn. He described its actions as emanations from "the red fool-fury of the Seine." He queried rhetorically: "Who is it that admires, and from the heart is attached to, national representative assemblies, but must turn with horror and disgust from such a profane burlesque and abominable perversion of that sacred institution?"

The effect of these fulminations, coming from the pen of a man who had bravely and effectively championed the American cause against Britain in the 1770's, was prodigious. All at once, without warning, the heroic leader of liberty against tyranny had become the defender of tyranny against liberty. So at least it seemed to English liberals, who were shocked by what they regarded as a shameful apostasy.

None was more shocked and saddened than Joseph Priestley, whose reply, *Letters to Burke*, was published within a few weeks after the first edition of the *Reflections* (there would be eleven editions the first year) had appeared. In the Preface he wrote:

> It is with very sensible regret that I find Mr. Burke and myself on two opposite sides of any important question, and especially that I must now no longer class him among the friends of what I deem to be *the cause of liberty, civil* or *religious*, after having, in a pleasing occasional intercourse of many years, considered him in this respectable light.... That an avowed friend of the American revolution should be an enemy of the French, which arose from

the same general principles, and in a great measure sprung from it, is to me unaccountable.

In the body of the work he concentrated his fire on remarks Burke had made concerning the civil establishment of religion, arguing that true religion did not need or want any such support, and he made a spirited defense of the National Assembly. The world was entering a new era, he said, one that was happier than any known before: "Together with the general prevalence of true principles of civil government, we may expect to see the extinction of all *national prejudice* and enmity, and the establishment of *universal peace* and goodwill among all nations."

The events of the immediately following months gave far more credence to Burke's dire predictions than to Priestley's hopeful ones, in the opinion of most Englishmen. The excesses of the French Revolution began to horrify the temperamentally moderate and conservative English as early as the spring of 1791. A fear began to grow —carefully nurtured, of course, by the upholders of political conservatism and religious orthodoxy—that atheistic Jacobinism might spread across the Channel and wreak such havoc in England as it threatened to do in France. Burke came to seem more and more a wise prophet who warned his countrymen of grave dangers—the danger of external aggression from an ancient national enemy and the even more terrifying danger of internal subversion from such radicals as Priestley, whom Burke attacked in the House of Commons.

Nowhere in England were such fears greater or stronger than in Birmingham as the summer of 1791 came on. Party feeling between Whigs and Tories and religious feeling between Churchmen and Dissenters were here especially bitter, exacerbated by the polemical manners of the irrepressible Priestley. He was not always fortunate in his choice of metaphor. In his *Familiar Letters Addressed to the Inhabitants of Birmingham,* designed to gain support for repeal of the Test Acts, he had written:

> We are, as it were, laying gunpowder, grain by grain, under the old building of error and superstition, which a single spark may hereafter inflame, so as to produce an instantaneous explosion; in consequence of which that edifice, the erection of which has been the work of ages, may be overturned in a moment, and so effectually as that the same foundation can never be built upon again.

Such words, much quoted out of context (they had been read aloud in the House of Commons), rang ominously in the ears of many Birminghamians in July, 1791. Priestley was a revolutionary, as well as a heretic! He must be suppressed, by violence if need be.

On the eleventh of that month there appeared in a Birmingham newspaper an advertisement of a dinner to be held in the leading hotel on July 14 "to commemorate the auspicious day [Bastille Day] which witnessed the Emancipation of Twenty-six Millions of People from the yoke of Despotism. . . ." Tickets would be "5s each, including a Bottle of Wine," and dinner would be "on the Table at Three o'clock precisely." In the same newspaper, immediately below the dinner advertisement, appeared one which offered for sale on Friday, July 15, for "ONE HALF-PENNY" an "AUTHENTIC List of all those who" had dined the day before "in Commemoration of the French Revolution." This obvious effort to intimidate with a threat of personal violence was increased in effectiveness by an anonymous seditious handbill, purported to be in support of the French Revolution, which the arrangers of the Bastille Day dinner felt compelled publicly to disown. In a newspaper advertisement on July 13 they declared "their entire disapprobation of all such hand-bills and their ignorance of the authors," asserting that they "can only be intended to create distrust concerning the intention of the meeting, to disturb its harmony and inflame the minds of the people." In these circumstances, those who had arranged the dinner decided to cancel it and had gone so far as to send a handbill to the printer announcing this fact when they were dissuaded by the owner of the hotel. He was sure there was no danger of "tumult" provided "the gentlemen . . . took care to break up early."

Accordingly, the dinner was held the next day, Thursday, July 14. Eighty-one men attended it, and they entered and left the hotel without being disturbed. A crowd of men in an ugly mood had gathered near the hotel, however, by the time the meeting broke up and continued to loiter there for sometime afterward. Did they await Priestley? Did they believe he was afraid to come out of the hotel? The evidence is that they did and that he, who had prudently declined to attend the celebration, would have been roughly handled, had he then appeared.

At eight o'clock that evening a crowd again gathered before the hotel, growing soon into a liquor-inflamed mob, whose leaders directed them with suspicious precision first to the New Meetinghouse where Priestley preached, which was sacked and burned, and then to the Old Meetinghouse, which was likewise sacked and burned. No effort was made by the authorities to control the mob. Indeed, it was suspected that several magistrates actually encouraged them, and it is certain that the rallying cry of the mobsters was "Church and King!"

Priestley was playing backgammon with his wife after supper that evening, when an excited friend burst in to inform him that a murderous mob of thousands (it was truly murderous by this time) was on the way to Fairhill and might arrive at any moment. The good doctor found this hard to believe, but he and his wife finally climbed into his friend's chaise, taking with them "nothing more than the clothes we happened to have on." [6] They were so little apprehensive of the real danger they were in, however, that they stopped at a friend's house only a mile up the road and prepared to spend the night. There, at midnight, another excited message arrived. The mob was gathering at Priestley's house and would certainly proceed from there to the house where he then was. So once more, this time with his erstwhile host and family, he fled, but again for only a little way. They all stopped at another friend's house a bare half mile farther up the road. It stood on rising ground, this house: the air of the moonlit night was perfectly still, and so Priestley distinctly heard (as he himself later wrote) "all that passed at . . . [my] house, every shout of the mob, and almost every stroke of the instruments they had provided for breaking the doors and furniture." [7]

An eyewitness claimed that the good doctor heard these blows "undaunted," that he remained "tranquil and serene" as his invaluable laboratory and books and as yet unpublished manuscripts were destroyed.[8] All the same he suffered each blow as a deep hurt, from which even his buoyant spirit could never fully recover. Four days later he was in London, his home now burned, along with those of many of his fellow Dissenters; troops had had to be called out to quell the Birmingham riots. From London he sent to a Birmingham newspaper an open letter "To the Inhabitants of the Town of Birmingham." He wrote in part:

> . . . you have been misled. . . . By the discourses of your teachers, and the exclamations of your superiors in general, drinking confusion and damnation to us (which is well known to have been their frequent practice), your bigotry has been excited to the highest pitch, and nothing has been said to you to moderate your passions, but everything to

inflame them. . . . You have destroyed the most truly valuable and useful apparatus of philosophical instruments that perhaps any individual in this or any other country was ever possessed of, in my use of which I annually spent large sums, with no pecuniary view whatever, but only in the advancement of science, for the benefit of my country and of mankind. You have destroyed a library corresponding to that apparatus which no money can repurchase, except in the course of time. But what I feel far more, you have destroyed *manuscripts,* which have been the result of the laborious study of many years, and which I shall never be able to recompose; and this you have done to one who never did, or imagined you, any harm.

He never saw Birmingham again. The feeling against him in the town remained too high; his life would have been forfeit had he returned there to make his home, as at first he wished to do. He was not, in fact, safe in London. For several weeks the friends who sheltered him would not permit him to appear in the streets. He was moved to Tottenham in August and at last, in October, took (or had taken for him) a house in Hackney. His landlord was reluctant to rent to him, fearing mob violence—and not without reason. During the following months Priestley was again verbally attacked by Burke in the Commons, burned in effigy, cruelly caricatured in broadsides, and excoriated from hundreds of pulpits. He received insulting and even threatful letters by the score. His friends stood steadfastly beside him—he had a special genius for friendship—but they were few compared with his enemies, who included most of those powerful in the country.

In 1793 began the war between England and France which was not to end (although it was interrupted by a brief truce in 1802 and 1803) until the Battle of Waterloo, twenty-two years later. Early in the preceding year, wholly uncowed by his persecutors, Priestley had "gratefully" accepted the "honor of *citizenship*" in the French nation, offered by the French government, and he had declined to serve in the forthcoming French National Convention, to which he had been elected by the department of Orne, only from "a sense of my incapacity to discharge the duties of it . . . on account of my not being sufficiently acquainted with your language, and the particular circumstances of your country." Thus, he was a citizen of two nations that were at war with each other and was for the moment (he might not have survived the Terror) much more welcome in France than in his native land.

He actually considered emigration to France, where the government offered him the use of a monastery near Toulouse, after the British government began to arrest and imprison people for "seditious utterances" that were akin to his own published views. His position in Britain was no longer tenable. If he were not arrested by the government, he might at any moment become again a victim of mob violence, for the popular hatred of him now flared higher than ever. Even the Royal Society had rejected him: At least, several of his colleagues there had turned their backs on him in his troubles so that he had felt forced at last to resign his membership. France, however, seemed not to hold the answer. His sons, unable to find employment in England because of his notoriety, decided to emigrate to America, and in the end, he and his wife decided to do the same.

Death Comes to Doctor Priestley

They sailed from Gravesend on the *Samson,* April 7, 1794, having said good-bye forever to old and dear friends. Priestley was then just two weeks past his sixty-first birthday. They landed in New York on June 4: Priestley was on the high seas when Lavoisier went to his death at the guillotine in the Place de la Révolution.

His fame had long preceded him to the New World. He was made to feel very welcome in New York. But after two weeks he proceeded with his wife to Philadelphia, then the capital of the United States. He had less liking for Philadelphia than for New York, despite the warm welcome he received from Benjamin Rush, the great physician, and other members of the American Philosophical Society, which Franklin had founded and of which Priestley had for many years been an absentee member. The hot humid summer climate was oppressive, and epidemic yellow fever was a constant menace. Mrs. Priestley's aversion to the city amounted to horror. They therefore moved some 130 miles north of Philadelphia to the small town of Northumberland (it contained 100 houses in 1794), and there, on a high bank overlooking the Susquehanna River, Priestley began to build in the autumn of 1794 the house which would be his home for the remainder of his life.

Nearly twelve months passed, however, before the house was habitable, and by that time Priestley had suffered two great sorrows. In the early winter his youngest son, Harry, died—a blow all the harder to bear because it was the first sorrow of this nature he had had put on him. And in September, 1795, his wife died and was buried beside her son in the Friends' Graveyard. From that time on, Priestley's desire to live was much diminished, although he hoped he might visit England once before he died. He remained a very active, busy man—preaching, writing, and experimenting in the laboratory he had managed to establish—but the old fire and the old cheerfulness were gone from him. He spoke with unwonted sadness of his "exile" when he wrote to friends in England, and he suffered from a lack of congenial society in Northumberland. He planned to spend two winter months each year in Philadelphia and was generally able to do so.

It was while he was in Philadelphia, in 1801, that he was struck down by the first serious illness of his life. He came very near to death and never fully recovered his health. His digestion was permanently impaired. In November, 1803, his illness recurred, and he knew that it would be his last. He continued to work at his writing (in 1800 he had published his last scientific work, entitled *Doctrine of Phlogiston Established*) even after February 4, 1804, when he could no longer rise to dress and shave himself. On February 5, in the evening, he had his grandchildren brought to his bedside for prayers, giving to each of them his blessing. Early the next morning he called to his son, asking him to take down at his dictation certain additions he wished to make to the proof sheets of a theological work which was then in press. It is said that he dictated with perfect clarity and precision. "That is right," he said, when the dictation was read back to him. "I have now done."

A half hour later he died. He had put his hand to his face so that his son Joseph and Joseph's wife, who sat beside him, would not notice his passing. A considerable time elapsed before they realized that they were sitting beside his corpse.

Notes

Introduction

1. Bertrand Russell, *The Scientific Outlook* (New York, W. W. Norton, 1930), p. 265.
2. Quoted by Alfred North Whitehead, *Science and the Modern World* (New York, New American Library, 1948), Mentor ed., p. 12.
3. Russell, *loc. cit.*

Chapter 1 *Joseph Priestley: From Fieldhead to Bowood*

1. Joseph Priestley, *Memoirs of Dr. Joseph Priestley, written by himself, with a continuation to the time of his decease, by his son, Joseph Priestley* (London, 1806), p. 3. It has not seemed to the present author necessary to give page sources for further quotations made of this memoir.
2. Quoted by T. E. Thorpe, *Joseph Priestley* (New York, Dutton, 1906), p. 2.
3. Quoted by Anne Holt, *A Life of Joseph Priestley* (London, Oxford University Press, Humphrey Milford, 1931), p. 4.
4. Thorpe, *op. cit.*, quoting Timothy Priestley's reminiscences of his brother Joseph's boyhood, p. 8.
5. *Ibid.*, p. 18, quoting the Rev. Mr. Hargrove's account of Priestley in *The Inquirer* (London) for January 16, 1904.
6. A. S. Turberville, ed., *Johnson's England, an Account of the Life and Manners of His Age* (Oxford, Oxford University Press, 1933), Vol. II, p. 258.
7. Goldwin Smith, *The United Kingdom, a Political History* (London, Macmillan, 1899), Vol. II, p. 231.
8. *Ibid.*
9. According to portraits of him, notably the portrait in the Science Museum, London, reproduced as Illustration 152 in A. Wolf, *A History of Science, Technology and Philosophy in the 18th Cen-*

tury, 2d ed. (London, George Allen and Unwin, 1952), between pp. 342–43.

Chapter 2 *Antoine Lavoisier: The Making of a Scientist*

1. Sidney J. French, *Torch and Crucible, the Life and Death of Antoine Lavoisier* (Princeton, Princeton University Press, 1941), p. 17.

2. Gaetano Salvemini, *The French Revolution* (London, Jonathan Cape, 1954), p. 40.

3. Georg Brandes, *Voltaire,* trans. by Otto Kruger and Pierce Butler (New York, Albert and Charles Boni, 1930), Vol. II, p. 183.

4. French, *op. cit.,* pp. 45–46.

5. Quoted by Harold Nicolson, *The Age of Reason* (New York, Doubleday, 1961), p. 276.

6. The influence of Joseph Black's work on Lavoisier, generally believed to have been great, is deemed negligible by Henry Guerlac, *Lavoisier—The Crucial Year, the Background and Origin of His Experiments on Combustion in 1772* (Ithaca, Cornell University Press, 1961). Guerlac argues from considerable, but not incontrovertible, evidence that Black's *Experiments Upon Magnesia Alba,* being virtually unknown in France, was therefore almost certainly unknown to Lavoisier when he began his earliest great work in pneumatic chemistry.

Chapter 3 *Priestley the Experimenter*

1. Jean Rey, *The Increase in Weight of Tin and Lead on Calcination (1630)* (Edinburgh, William F. Clay, 1895), Alembic Club Reprints, No. 11, p. 36.

2. James Campbell Brown, *History of Chemistry,* 2d ed., Henry Hilton Brown, ed. (London, J. and A. Campbell, 1920), p. 231.

3. *Ibid.,* p. 232, quoting Georg Ernst Stahl's *Specimen Becherianum* (1702).

4. Rey, *op. cit.,* p. 10, argues in Essay IV that "Air and Fire are heavy, and move naturally downwards." Fire arises in air, not because it possesses levity, but because it is less dense than air. "If there were a tube extending from the centre of the earth far upwards into the region of fire, open at both ends and filled with the four elements, each in its ordinary position, then if we with-

drew the earth from beneath, the water would descend to occupy its place, leaving its own in the air, whose place would then be occupied by fire."

5. Joseph Priestley, *Considerations on the Doctrine of Phlogiston, and the Decomposition of Air* (1796), combined with Jon McLean, *Two Lectures on Combustion and an Examination of Doctor Priestley's Considerations on the Doctrine of Phlogiston,* William Foster, ed. (Princeton, Princeton University Press, 1929), first page of Introduction.

6. Thorpe, *op. cit.,* p. 168. Thorpe contrasts Priestley as a social, political and theological reformer ("always in advance of his time, receptive, fearless and insistent") with Priestley as a scientist ("timorous and halting when he might well be bold, conservative and orthodox when almost every other active worker was heterodox and progressive").

7. Arthur Pap, *Elements of Analytic Philosophy* (New York, Macmillan, 1949), p. 239.

8. Joseph Priestley, *Experiments and Observations on Different Kinds of Air,* Vol. 1 (London, 1774), pp. 50–54.

9. *Ibid.,* p. 111.

Chapter 4 *Lavoisier the Systematizer*

1. James Bryant Conant, ed., *Harvard Case Studies in Experimental Science* (Cambridge, Harvard University Press, 1957), Vol. I, pp. 85–86.

2. Quoted by French, *op. cit.,* p. 104.

3. Douglas McKie, *Antoine Lavoisier, the Father of Modern Chemistry* (Philadelphia, J. B. Lippincott, 1935), p. 220.

4. Quoted by French, *op. cit.,* p. 159.

5. McKie, *op. cit.,* p. 258.

Chapter 5 *Lavoisier and the French Revolution*

1. Guerlac, *op. cit.,* pp. 146–55, tells of a letter Turgot wrote Condorcet on August 16, 1771, in which Turgot proposed a theory of combustion strikingly similar to that Lavoisier was then beginning to develop. Turgot had studied chemistry under Rouelle, Lavoisier's teacher. Guerlac thinks it unlikely that

Lavoisier ever learned of Turgot's "striking anticipation" of his own theory.

2. Quoted by French, *op. cit.*, p. 278.

3. *Ibid.*, p. 219.

4. Quoted by McKie, *op. cit.*, p. 278.

Chapter 6   *Doctor Priestley Dies in Exile*

1. Holt, *op. cit.*, p. 126.

2. Henry Carrington Bolton, ed., *Scientific Correspondence of Joseph Priestley* (New York, privately printed, 1892), p. 201.

3. Holt, p. 32. Also, Thorpe, *op. cit.*, pp. 103–105.

4. Quoted by Thorpe, *op. cit.*, p. 93.

5. Samuel Smiles, *Lives of the Engineers: Boulton and Watt* (London, John Murray, 1904), p. 383.

6. Joseph Priestley, *Appeal to the Public on the Subject of the Riots in Birmingham* (London, 2nd edition, 1792), p. 29. Quoted by Holt, *op. cit.*, p. 159.

7. Priestley, *op. cit.*, p. 30. Quoted by Holt, *op. cit.*, p. 160.

8. Martha Russell, *Christian Reformer*, May, 1835, issue, Vol. II, p. 293 ff. Quoted by Thorpe, *op. cit.*, pp. 129–133, and by Holt, *op. cit.*, pp. 163–168.

Bibliography

Becker, Carl L., *The Heavenly City of the Eighteenth Century Philosophers*. New Haven, Yale University Press, 1932.

Black, Joseph, *Experiments Upon Magnesia Alba, Quicklime, and Some Other Alcaline Substances* (1755). Alembic Club Reprints, No. 1. Edinburgh, William F. Clay, 1898.

Bolton, Henry Carrington, ed., *Scientific Correspondence of Joseph Priestley*. New York, privately printed, 1892.

Brown, James Campbell, *A History of Chemistry*, second edition edited by Henry Hilton Brown. London, J. and A. Churchill, 1920.

Cavendish, Henry, *Experiments on Air*. Alembic Club Reprints, No. 3. Edinburgh, William F. Clay, 1895.

Conant, James Bryant, ed., *Harvard Case Studies in Experimental Science*, Vol. I. Cambridge, Harvard University Press, 1957.

Crowther, J. G., *Scientists of the Industrial Revolution*. Philadelphia, Dufour Editions, 1963.

Foster, William, ed., *Considerations on the Doctrine of Phlogiston, and the Decomposition of Water,* and *Two Lectures on Combustion and an Examination of Doctor Priestley's Considerations on the Doctrine of Phlogiston*. Princeton, Princeton University Press, 1941.

French, Sidney J., *Torch and Crucible, the Life and Death of Antoine Lavoisier*. Princeton, Princeton University Press, 1941.

Gaxotte, Pierre, *The French Revolution*. New York, Scribner's, 1932.

Grimaux, Édouard, *Lavoisier, 1743-1794*. Paris, Alcan, 1888. (In French)

The Grolier Club, *Catalogue of Printed Work by and Memorabilia of Antoine Laurent Lavoisier, 1743-1794*. New York, The Grolier Club, 1952.

Guerlac, Henry, *Lavoisier—The Crucial Year, the Background and Origin of His Experiments on Combustion in 1772*. Ithaca, Cornell University Press, 1961.

Holt, Anne, *A Life of Joseph Priestley*. London, Oxford University Press, Humphrey Milford, 1931.

Koestler, Arthur, *The Sleepwalkers*. New York, Macmillan, 1959.

Lavoisier, Antoine, *Elements of Chemistry* (1789). Reprinted in *Great Books of the Western World*, Vol. I. Chicago, Encyclopaedia Britannica, Inc., 1952.

Lefebvre, Georges, *The French Revolution, From Its Origins to 1793*. New York, Columbia University Press, 1962.

―――― *The French Revolution, From 1793 to 1799*. New York, Columbia University Press, 1964.

Lenard, Philipp, *Great Men of Science*. London, Macmillan, 1933.

McKenzie, A. E. E., *The Major Achievements of Science*, Vol. I. Cambridge, England, The University Press, 1960.

McKie, Douglas, *Antoine Lavoisier, the Father of Modern Chemistry*. Philadelphia, Lippincott, 1935.

Mason, S. F., *Main Currents of Scientific Thought*. New York, Abelard-Schuman, 1958.

Mathiez, Albert, *The French Revolution*, New York, Alfred A. Knopf, 1927.

Meyer, Ernst Von, *A History of Chemistry*. London, Macmillan, 1891.

Priestley, Joseph, *Experiments and Observations on Different Kinds of Air*. London, 6 vols., 1774-86.

Salvemini, Gaetano, *The French Revolution, 1788-1792*. London, Jonathan Cape, 1954.

Schwartz, George, and Bishop, Philip W., ed., *Moments of Discovery*, Vol. I. *The Origins of Science*. New York, Basic Books, 1958.

Smiles, Samuel, *Lives of the Engineers: Boulton and Watt*. London, John Murray, 1904.

Teton, René, ed., *The Beginnings of Modern Science, From 1450 to 1800*. New York, Basic Books, 1964.

Thorpe, T. E., *Joseph Priestley*. New York, Dutton, 1906.

Thorpe, T. E., *Essays in Historical Chemistry*. London, Macmillan, 1902.

Tilden, Sir William A., *Famous Chemists, The Men and Their Work*. London, George Rutledge, 1921.

Van Doren, Carl, *Benjamin Franklin*. New York, Viking Press, 1938.

Wightman, William P. D., *The Growth of Scientific Ideas*. New Haven, Yale University Press, 1953.

Wolf, A., *A History of Science, Technology and Philosophy in the 18th Century*, 2d ed. London, George Allen and Unwin, 1952.

———— *A History of Science, Technology and Philosophy in the 16th and 17th Centuries*. Harper Torch Book. New York, Harper and Row, 1959.

Index

29. 1/05

NOV 18 1966 3

QD
22
L4D3

947632

21 6/98

Please Do Not Remove Cards From Pocket

YOUR LIBRARY CARD
may be used at all library agencies. You
are, of course, responsible for all materials
checked out on it. As a courtesy to others
please return materials promptly — before
overdue penalties are imposed.

The SAINT PAUL PUBLIC LIBRARY